MUDDLING THROUGH

MUDDLING THROUGH
OR BRITAIN IN A NUTSHELL

By THEODORA BENSON
and BETTY ASKWITH

NICOLAS BENTLEY drew the pictures

LONDON · VICTOR GOLLANCZ · 1936

First published October 1936
Second impression December 1936

Printed in Great Britain by
The Camelot Press Ltd., London and Southampton

CONTENTS

England and Wales

5

CONTENTS

Ireland

Scotland

7

LIST OF ILLUSTRATIONS

England and Wales

BM

9

Ireland

Scotland

HISTORY

CHARACTERISTICS

GEOGRAPHY

INSTITUTIONS

ENGLAND and WALES

Really foreigners are funny—

INTRODUCTION

Last year we usefully performed the task of explaining and clarifying the world. We did it in a book called *Foreigners, or the World in a Nutshell*. Mr. Nicolas Bentley gave us valuable help in bringing home to readers the facts of nationality. We included in this volume a very condensed essay upon the English. Thoughtful students have asked us to deal more thoroughly with this subject; to collect and to exhibit in convenient form all that is known about the English and their land. It is but reasonable that they should be given as much space as the rest of the world and all its peoples together, and they are badly in need of explaining and clarifying.

But we must take you into our confidence before we begin. *Foreigners* turned out to be a Funny book. We were surprised by this, but we were gratified, as it proved that we had Sense of

13

Humour, the greatest virtue of our country and our generation. Now we are called upon to repeat our coup. You see our predicament. Foreigners just are funny. The English are not.

—Aren't they?

IDEALS

Humour

" Smile ! darn you, smile "

Humour is one of the most important English ideals, because where should we all be without it ? This is a question that has

16

never been answered. English sense of humour is one of the things that won the war; even America in claiming that she won the war, has never had the nerve to attribute it to *her* sense of humour.

Sense of humour is a very exclusive quality. Only the English have it. Foreigners sometimes have wit, fun and a sense of the ridiculous, they are sometimes amusing and amused, they are sometimes good company. But humour—no; that is an attribute beyond foreigners; it is even beyond dogs.

Though sense of humour is undoubtedly a national attribute, and it is well known (in England) that the English have it, you will find if you consider the circle of your acquaintance that though they sometimes have wit, fun and a sense of the ridiculous, though they are sometimes amusing and amused, though they are sometimes good company, only you in a truly-proportioned and fundamental way have a real sense of humour.

You will see at once that it is a very high ideal.

Muddling Through

This is a very important ideal. If we did not muddle THROUGH it would show a lack of grit and indeed of that success necessary to a top nation. If we did not MUDDLE through it would show that we had that slick, cheap, unprincipled cleverness that foreigners so often have. Also—and this is very important—if we did not muddle through it would show that we were really trying.

Conventionality

It is bad form to be conspicuous.

Unconventionality

It is bad form to care.

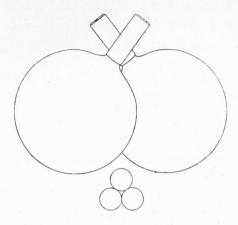

Sportsmanship

The whole of British education and tradition is designed to teach Britons not to show that they mind losing at games, and not to cry.

In every field of endeavour you should always choose the worst weapons and give every possible advantage to your opponent. Even if he then beats you, you don't look an ass, because it's rather unsporting of him.

Foreigners are not sportsmen.

COUNTIES

Yorkshire

Yorkshire has pudding.

It is the largest county in England. It has ridings. It has moors and dales. These are wild, bleak and grand. The Yorkshire accent is not quite the same as the Lancashire accent, and though funny, it is less funny. You cannot, however, reproduce any difference. Yorkshiremen are pre-eminently hardheaded. They are plain, bluff and practical, and they are North country, which seems to be creditable. " Art coomin', laad ? " they inquire of one another.

York has an Archbishop and a Minster. In history it had a rose.

Yorkshire had the Brontës, and has the Brontë country. It has Priestley. Even in Yorkshire patience has its limits, and there is no Priestley country.

Lancashire

Lancashire is in the North country, and all over the music halls. See Wigan. Also see Blackpool. Be sure to see Manchester. It has a very splendid funny accent. The veriest nitwit imitating a Lancashire accent can be recognised as imitating a Lancashire accent, even if it turns out to be pure Yorkshire. See Cockneys. If desired, see Yorkshire. Lancashire has the cotton trade (finished) and Liverpool Cathedral (unfinished), and a lot of docks and Morecambe Bay shrimps.

Lancaster had an historical rose, but this is not exclusive as York was in the same racket. Lancashire undisputedly has Gracie Fields. A Lancashire observation is " Eh, ba goom."

23

Lincolnshire

Lincolnshire is flat and has little Holland.

Lincolnshire has a poacher.

The Midlands and the Shires

The Midlands and the Shires are the heart of England, and have any amount of hunting country. This is very important. See hunting.

" Which way, what ? "

Rutland

Rutland is the smallest county of England.

Norfolk

Norfolk is flat. It has fens, and as though that were not enough, it has broads. Naturally it has jackets.

Shropshire

Shropshire has a lad who is generally hanging at X roads or alternatively in the county jail. If he is not doing this he is pretty sure to be in the Army or to have committed suicide. In his lighter moments he gets girls into trouble or lies down in lovely muck. It is all strangely beautiful.

Sussex

Sussex is one of the best known English counties owing to the poets and novelists. The only thing is that Sussex itself has got somewhat overlaid with the poets and novelists and on hearing the word one hardly conjures up any clear picture but simply babbles something about Rudyard Kipling and Sheila Kaye-Smith. However it is known that Sussex has downs and dew-ponds and some ancient old shepherds. Possibly it has a Weald whatever that may be, but that is more certainly Kent.

Wessex

Wessex is the Hardy country. It is full of places like Caster-bridge and some very splendid peasants. It has wild Beauty and Tragedies. Far less is known about it than used to be the case.

Hardy Country

27

"Drake is on his stomach and a thousand miles away——"

Devonshire

Devonshire—Devon to the Romantics—is one of the best known English counties. It is red, that is to say its soil is red, it has lanes, and it has cream. Pre-eminently it has Francis—Frankie to the poets—Drake, and a race of tough bluff briny mariners known as Devon men or sometimes Devon sea-dogs. They and all the other Devonians talk dialect. They say yew, tew and füle (see Zummerset). Devon also has Dartmoor, with convicts, Exmoor, most of which is in Somerset but that doesn't count, but not Lammermoor. It has Plymouth, and Plymouth has a hoe on which Francis (Frankie) Drake played Bowls.

28

Somerset

Not much is known about Somerset except that it is generally known in comic songs as Zummerset. This is because of local dialect (see Devon). The most famous of these songs is about a grey mare with rather a varied crew of riders. Only some people know this song to be Devonshire. It depends on geography really.

Horse-riding in Somerset (or Devon)

29

Cornwall

The most salient fact that leaps to all our minds about Cornwall is that it is shaped like a boot. It has a lizard and St. Michael's Mount. It has cream, not so pre-eminently but in a rather more connoisseurish way than Devon. All Cornish names begin with Tre or Pol or Pen. And should Trelawney die it is very well known that fifty thousand Cornishmen would like to ask somebody, possibly the Government, a question. It is not known whether or not Trelawney deceased. Cornwall has pixies. The Cornish prefer to call them piskies. We do not know why.

Kent

Kent is the Garden of England, but then what isn't? A man of Kent is quite different from a Kentish man. What difference it makes and what the distinction is, is not known. Nor is it known whether there is any ruling in force in the county about distinctions between women.

Wales

A Lover of Leeks

Wales is much larger even than Yorkshire, but you cannot really count it as the largest county in England as it has several smaller counties of its own. Besides, the Welsh are not English.

31

Wales is beautiful and has mountains and sea coast and beauty spots. It has Snowdon.

The Welsh are all Celts and all that follows emerges quite naturally from this fact. They are mostly small and dark and some are red haired. Shakespeare had a famous Welshman who was very fiery, but it is not actually known whether the Welsh now are fiery or not. They have beautiful soft sing song voices, and they also sing a great deal, beautifully. They mostly speak English but they also have a language of their own—Welsh—which they use a good deal in naming their towns and villages. No one except the Welsh can pronounce this language as all the words are very long with an incredible number of consonants (many of them, especially ls, doubled) and no vowels. On the other hand Welsh proper names are very simple. The very worst of them is Llewellyn, and the rest are Evan, Lloyd, Jones, Owen and Morgan. (Morgan should not be confused with Megan, which is the Welsh female Christian name, corresponding to the masculine Taffy.) Even the introduction of the variants Effan and Chones—a form of Welsh pronunciation thoughtfully invented by the English to put Welsh people at their ease—does not complicate it very much.

Nevertheless, you can always trust a Celt to complicate anything. The Welsh do not, like the Chinese, all look alike (except to the Chinese) but they all sound alike, because their names are Llewellyn Jones Llewellyn, and Jones Llewellyn Jones, and Evan Lloyd Evan Lloyd Lloyd Evans, and Lloyd Evan Evan Evan Lloyd, and Owen Owen, and so on indefinitely.

The Welsh steal and the Welsh lie without exception of time or person. This however is more inconvenient than contemptible of them. It is one of those facts that are so very well known and characteristic that it has attained a certain dignity; like elephants never forgetting an injury, which at first sight you might wrongly conclude to show them lacking in Christian spirit. If you trust a Welshman and he robs and deceives, only you are to blame. He has acted as his nature imperatively dictated to him. The Welsh are not unlovable.

The Welsh are of course poetic, being Celts, and probably feel beauty in a more cissy way than you and I. Even at football matches they wear daffodils and sing. They had a distinctive national dress (unlike the English) but have rather let it die out (unlike the Scotch). It consisted of elongated vertical hats and red shawls, and was rather chivalrously reserved for women.

They had Owen Glendower. They have Lloyd George. Their patron saint liked leeks.

Eisteddfod

33

DISTRICTS

The Potteries

The Potteries, very reasonably, produce pottery.

The Dukeries

Do the Dukeries, equally reasonably, produce Dukes?

The Black Country

The Black Country is artificially black and rather derelict. It has disused slag heaps.

The North Country

For the North Country, see Yorkshire, and Lancashire. There is also Westmorland and Durham and Cumberland, but they don't count.

The Lake District

The Lake District has lakes, and Windermere. It had Words-worth. It also had Coleridge, but less so.

Daffodils, etc.

LONDON

1. Fogs

We have the best fogs in the world.

The Pride of the Constables' College

2. Police

Our London Police are wonderful. This is not so much a thing that we know, as a thing that we know that Americans and Continentals know.

3. Cockneys

Cockneys are poor people born within the sound of Bow Bells. They are the salt of the earth. They have a dialect that is justly popular because when you imitate it people know that you are talking Cockney (see Lancashire). Cockneys are good-natured, shrewd, plucky, quick as a knife and very witty. Examples of Cockney humour: " Garn," and " You're another."

4. Sights

Piccadilly Circus is the centre of the world. If you wait there long enough you see everyone in the world, but this is difficult to do because of getting hungry, and because of getting moved on (see Police).

London Bridge is broken down. It is known however that all the difficulty is really about Waterloo Bridge.

The Strand is the centre of the world (see Piccadilly Circus). People who know what's what go down it to have bananas.

Famous people are buried in Westminster Abbey.

The Houses of Parliament have Parliament and Big Ben.

St. Paul's has a dome and was built by Sir Christopher Wren (probably not unaided). It is falling down.

The Guards change at Buckingham Palace.

Harrison Ainsworth and all That

The Albert Hall and the Albert Memorial commemorate Albert. For a long time it has been the thing to consider them hideous. But be on your guard : our prophecy is that it will soon be highbrow to admire them.

Kew has lilac time.

The Tower has the Bloody Tower and the Yeomen of the Guard and the Crown Jewels. The Yeomen of the Guard are beef eaters.

The Parks are the lungs of London. Bushey Park has Chestnuts. Kensington Gardens has Peter Pan. Hyde Park is shut at midnight but it is sometimes too late.

Bond Street is expensive.

Regent Street is spoilt (see Park Lane).

Park Lane is spoilt (see Regent Street).

5. Famous Houses of London

The famous houses of London are all pulled down.

6. Scotland Yard

Scotland Yard is not in Scotland and may not be a yard. It is what fails to solve crime mysteries before an amateur detective is called in.

7. The London Season

Important features of the London Season are Ascot, Goodwood and Cowes. All of these take place out of London.

TOWNS

"Pythagoras, my foot!"

Oxford

O Oxford, city of dreaming spires and lost causes !

Oxford has a lot of things. It has the Oxford Group and the Oxford Movement, and one of them (but not both) is the Oxford Group Movement. Then there is the Oxford accent which is what American comedians speak with when they take off the English. There were Oxford trousers. There is marmalade.

Oxford Dons are absent-minded, cultured, pernickety, eccentric and entirely out of touch with life. They have pedantic turns of speech and peculiar mannerisms. And there was, of course, Spooner.

There are also Undergraduates.

Cambridge

Cambridge always wins the boat race.

Cambridge has sausages.

Epsom

The Derby is run at Epsom. And what about those salts ?

Derby

The Derby is not run at Derby. When the Young Pretender found this, he turned back.

Cheltenham

Cheltenham is solely populated by Indian Colonels. There are races ; probably not in pursuit of an electric stingah.

Old Boys of the Old Brigade

Brighton

Brighton is on the sea. It has a Pavilion (don't see Marble Arch) and a vague Regency background. It also has several piers with slot machines, and the Metropole. You cannot talk about spending the week-end there without a certain amount of digging in the ribs. Most of the week-end visitors to Brighton are semi-decrepit invalids.

Wigan

Wigan has a pier. By this time either you **are** in fits of laughter or you are not, it is useless to labour the point.

Manchester

Manchester has cotton mills. It rains there. It is known as Ma-a-anchester.

Stratford

Stratford, which is on the Avon, has the Swan. Americans go there.

Bath

Bath is very lovely and complete and fragrant and eighteenth century and early nineteenth century. It has almost more things than is altogether fair. Besides the waters and the buns it has Beau Nash who wouldn't allow people to wear swords, and Sheridan and the Linleys and Jane Austen and even Sam Weller. It has Atmosphere and then some.

Gloucester

Gloucester has a tailor or nine. It has one or two limericks.

Blackpool

Blackpool has Wakes weeks. It has the Great Wheel and illuminations and cheaper return fares there than anywhere and simply lots of fun. There are a lot of jokes, such as finding garments you thought you'd lost because you put them on in the wrong order when you bathed there last year and hadn't seen them since.

Margate

Margate is the Blackpool of the South.

Clacton

And then of course there's Clacton. (Try looking under Music Hall.)

Melton

Melton is in the Shires (see the Shires). It is very smart, top-notch and absolutely the thing to hunt from Melton. It is also a little ostentatious, vulgarly rich and American. It all depends.

PERSONALITIES

Lord Lonsdale

Lord Lonsdale wears side-whiskers and smokes cigars. He has a yellow motor-car. He is a Sportsman and a Prince of Good Fellows. He practically lives in Bertram Mills' circus.

Noel Coward

Noel Coward is Brilliant. He is also young, satiric and vaguely a little unsound. He drinks cocktails. But if he goes on writing things like *Cavalcade* he may surmount all this.

The Play-boy of the West End World

George Robey

Mr. George Robey is the Prime Minister of Mirth. He demonstrates good broad vulgar fun in a dignified British way. He has (detachable) eyebrows. He will probably end by playing Hamlet in a longer and heavier version by A. P. Herbert.

Lord Beaverbrook

Lord Beaverbrook is a Canadian. He has a Press. He has Personality. He—oh well, perhaps we had better leave it at that.

Lord Beaverbrook

Stanley Baldwin

People are getting terribly tired of saying that Mr. Baldwin is Honest and that Mr. Baldwin Smokes a Pipe. A school of thought is growing up which says that Mr. Baldwin is a Deep 'Un, that he knows a thing or two, and they mention his name in connection with those well-known phenomena cartloads of monkeys. But there seems to be no way of getting round the pipe.

It is well known in the South that Mr. Baldwin is immensely popular in the North. What is known in the North is not known.

Some people think that Mr. Baldwin will retire at the Coronation. Ah—but whose ?

The Pipe and the Book

Neville Chamberlain

Mr. Neville Chamberlain will lead the National Party much better than Mr. Baldwin. Mr. Neville Chamberlain will lead the National Party much worse than Mr. Baldwin.

Anthony Eden

Mr. Anthony Eden is a mere boy of round about forty. He likes the League of Nations. He is very well dressed.

L. G.

Lloyd George

Lloyd George is Welsh. This to the charitable minded accounts for everything except possibly his long white hair. And even that perhaps is a thought Celtic.

James Maxton

" Jimmy " Maxton has nice long black hair which flops all over his face. All Conservative members tell you that he is a delightful, sincere chap and the greatest friend of everybody in the House of Commons and a splendid, topping fellow. From this you should deduce 1. The delightfulness of Mr. Maxton, and 2. The charming broad-mindedness of Conservative members.

Other Politicians

There are a lot of other politicians such as John Simon, Sam Hoare, Hore Belisha, Winston Churchill, Austen Chamberlain, Major Attlee, old uncle Lord Hailsham and all, whose names are familiar and who get into cartoons. But the things that are known about them are ephemeral and change from evening paper to evening paper. So that we cannot risk pinning them down even for the short while that it will take this book to go to press. Although of course Austen Chamberlain's eyeglass and Winston Churchill's hats and the fact that the whole bunch of them have been there so many many many years almost endears them to us and lends stability to the political horizon.

INSTITUTIONS

Portsmouth Points

The Navy

The Navy is splendid, the Navy is fine, the Navy is A1. Every nice girl loves a sailor, and this is natural for they are not only free and easy, bright and breezy, but they can dance the hornpipe, and have blue eyes, forty-seven of them are ginger-headed, and they are tattooed.

Some of the sailors who sail before the mast or below the deck or whatever the phrase is, are able-bodied. What of the rest? Midshipmen are known as " snotties," which seems far-fetched, and never, never as " middies," which would only be reasonable. Discipline is splendid and terrific and no naval officer can get through a sentence without saying " Sir " at least nine times. The Navy is both the Senior and the Silent Service. The Army is, of course, the Junior, but is it ever known as the Talkative Service?

America and Japan have some synthetic imitations but THE Navy is British.

The City and the Bank of England

The Bank of England is safe. It is the Old Lady of Threadneedle Street. No other bank can say either of these things. This has been a great difficulty in Europe and America.

The City is responsible for the credit of England, so that in a sense it is not only her purse but practically her good name as well. Land in the City is worth a terrific price, and you cannot get a good meal there. It is populated by stockbrokers and stock-jobbers and bill brokers and bill jobbers and other people like that. They are quite apt to be bosses and have secretaries.

The City has the Stock Exchange. The Stock Exchange has Bulls and Bears. Its resemblance to the Zoological Gardens does not quite end there, but nearly.

If an outsider goes into the Stock Exchange they take his trousers off. Outsider in this connection does not mean cad but simply non-member of the Stock Exchange.

City police wear different helmets and the King has to ask permission to come in.

The Weather

The English are, very rightly, rather inhibited conversation-alists. They do not get quickly down to personalities for fear of giving themselves away, and if they were to know anything about an intellectual subject it would be showing off and suspect to say so. But the English are not bores, and so ordinary weather that stayed put for quite a while would not suffice them as a topic for sustained speech. It is therefore a special and providential dispensation that the English have weather so remarkable as to be well worth talking about.

The English are proud of their weather because no foreign countries have weather anything like it. At least as a matter of fact several neighbouring countries have, but it doesn't quite count.

"Oh to be in England, now that April's there"

Class

Class in a way has made England what it is.

Everybody in England belongs to a different class. This is very soothing and satisfactory because it gives everybody an opportunity of looking down, in the most kindly and forgiving and unsuperior way, on a large number of other people. It would be supposed according to the laws of arithmetical progression that there must be someone at the very bottom who can't look down on anyone except foreigners, but no one has yet discovered who that is.

Another cosy thing about class is that by means of this system everyone knows exactly where he is. This saves an infinity of trouble and of pushing and scrambling. Even if you wish to be somewhere else it is an advantage to know where you start from.

Everyone in England is a snob, but with the usual English balance and sense of proportion it is a mistake to be one in such a flamboyant way as to get called one. For that is laughable.

An old county family is better than a new title, but we do like titles. It is the duty of people with hereditary titles to have children, though that is optional for those who have only looks and brains. The middle classes are the backbone of the country. You get on equally well with Dukes and chimney sweeps, but you can't stand the middle classes. There'll never be communism in England because the British working man has too much sense of humour. If you use the word refined you say refaned or refeened in inverted commas. People who say them without inverted commas are not your class.

Never speak of a serviette.

Democracy

England is an essentially democratic country as opposed to all those countries, republics and so on, which are merely democratic. (See Class.)

OVER—down under

Sport

Sport is an outward and visible symbol of sportsmanship. Apart from this it is in itself madly important.

Hunting, fishing and shooting are the three sports paramount, and it used to be quite a thing not to sound the final g's but that is now a little period. In a way hunting is the most sublime of them. The idea of sport is that it is for its own sake and quite unmaterial (like cricket) but in fishing and shooting you do rather hope to be left with something useful at the end of it. Then again, there is some slight element of danger in hunting, whereas among the best people the risk should be negligible out shooting, and it is merely silly to go fishing and get drowned.

Hunting is extremely county and clique-ish and correct. It is old-fashioned back-bone-of-the-country. It is fast-set and smart. It is delightfully democratic. Farmers like it. It gives the foxes a treat. The Pytchley is like a birdcage. You ought to ride straight.

Shooting is partridge and pheasant and grouse mostly in kind of relays called seasons. There is also a lot more, such as snipe and duck and black cock. But you have to be careful; it would not count, for instance, if you shot an albatross. Beaters you have and sometimes butts. A lot of it takes place in Scotland, where you rough it on picnics of champagne and foie gras and hot casserole in perfectly appointed barns (see Scotland). You rather hate shooting hares.

There are a great many jokes about fishing, largely about liars or about a lunatic addressing an angler from over the asylum wall. Fish are brown trout and rainbow trout and (see Scotland)

"*Yoicks!*

Tally-ho!

salmon. There is a tremendous variety of bait, but not all of it is etiquette for every occasion. Fish ought to be played.

Every Englishman should be keen on some kind of sport; in theory keenness is more important even than skill. If he doesn't go in for sport, he may be able to rehabilitate himself over games. A sportsman knows he is all right and can make any mere intellectual, no matter how brilliant, look silly and feel silly without even trying.

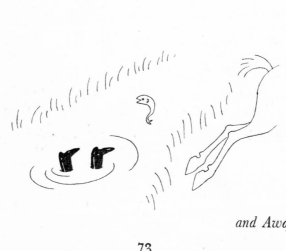

and Away!"

Foreigners have no word for sport. Though madly keen on it, panting in the footsteps of England, they are obliged to call it le sport. Which is very revealing.

" Punch " and " The Times "

After *Punch*, *The Times* is our leading serious newspaper.

Public Schools

The Public Schools have made England what she is. The Public School spirit runs the Empire. The playing fields of Eton were the direct cause of the well-known victory at Waterloo.

A boy is not sent to a Public School to have his head stuffed with pedantic knowledge but to learn to be a gentleman and possibly a Christian. This used to be done entirely by games, but there is now a section of the community among whom the all-sufficiency of games is blown upon. Some people think that boys should now be allowed to work at their books and even to write poetry without being persecuted. And the public schools

" Miserabile dictu ! "

themselves have grown far more tolerant so that there is much less bullying, if any. It is perhaps well that these views did not come into fashion prior to Waterloo.

There was a robust but narrow-minded time when it stamped a boy as a prig and a swot to work at his lessons and his life was made a burden in consequence if he did. Even in those days it was quite all right for one of maturer years to be a scholar; in fact, it often went with being a Christian and a gentleman.

Your schooldays were the happiest time of your life. The public school system grinds out all æsthetic ability and individuality, and turns sensitive, intelligent boys into neurotics or repressed escapists. The Public Schools are sinks of festering wickedness. Their clean wholesome discipline is what gives Englishmen their grit and sense of fair play.

Say what you like against our Public Schools—and it has quite lately become permissible for you to like to say quite a lot—the fact remains that foreigners don't have our public schools and that there is a far higher proportion of foreign cads. Foreigners are also clever and don't quite understand fair play.

Music Hall and Pantomime

Music Hall is funny and tremendously English. There are music halls in Paris and Berlin and Vaudeville shows in America, many of the artistes on the British Music Hall stage are foreigners, but none of this really counts. Cockney and Lancashire are tremendous features of the music hall, and where would you get them except in England ? People fall down a good deal, and though this and laughing at it is rather international, nowhere else is such art and such appreciation brought to bear on the matter. The Music Halls get dirtier and dirtier, hurrah, but luckily this doesn't count as they are so well known to be Temples of Good Clean Fun.

Crazy Month is a very English scheme by which Music Hall artistes can none of them finish their turns or do anything properly. It is so silly you have to laugh.

Pantomimes are not in pantomime. They are a form of Christmas Entertainment for children patronised chiefly by grown ups, and it is so well known that grown ups like them better that it's quite a surprise that children enjoy them too. They are a rather surréaliste treatment of fairy stories, and one of the things that is so good about them is that the hero is a girl and the dame is a man. The hero—principal boy—used to be a very bulging blonde girl, but now she is generally thin and any colouring is permissible. There is scope for music hall turns, and for spectacle and ballet, and there are newish songs and very old jokes. A great feature are the pantomime children, who have large legs, fringes and shrill cockney accents.

77

Pantomime is a grand form of entertainment, and it at least is purely and utterly English. Nowhere else would it be tolerated.

B.B.C.

The B.B.C. is always wrong.

"I beg yours"

Whimsicality

" James," we said to our kitten, " when is humour not humour and poetry not poetry and charm not charm ? "

He winked at us. *He* knew.

Our canary winked at us. *She* knew.

At that moment a cloud of fairies flew out of our hydrangea; *you* would have thought that they were bees, but we *saw* that they were fairies.

" Ten little pink toes under the gooseberry bushes," they sang, " ten little pink fingers under the gooseberry bushes."

And all the bells in Heaven started laughing.

Football

It is VERY well known that there will never be a revolution in England, because both sides would have to break off to go to the Cup-Tie.

Cricket

Cricket is long, dull, slow and boring. The English are proud of its being that way. No one else they feel would have a national game admitted by all to be long, dull, slow and boring. This constitutes a peculiar score for the English. It is part of the English Character. The English laugh heartily at such phrases as " it's not cricket " and " playing with a straight bat," but they are enabled to do so because they have no doubts at all of the utter rightness of the cricket ideal. We can and do laugh at cricket. But really it's a bit too thick the way those Australians keep on barracking.

" Beer is Best"

82

Beer

Beer, sometimes associated with skittles though actually more often seen in conjunction with darts, is our national drink. Beer is somehow noble. What is wrong with some of our upper classes is that they don't drink much beer but subsist on things like champagne and gin and cointreau, which are naturally decadent. Roman Catholic poets and professional humorists drink beer with tireless and praiseworthy perseverance.

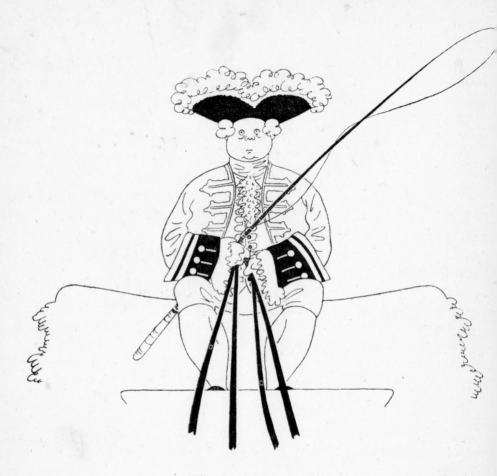

The Lord Mayor's Day

The Lord Mayor

The Lord Mayor lives in the Mansion House on turtle soup. Luckily only for a year as it must undermine the strongest constitution. He has a procession, a coachman and a day (the 9th of November, not to be confused with the day belonging to Mr. Fawkes).

The Lord Mayor is very special and the King has to ask him if he can drive through the City. This though it has no practical bearing is one of those quaint old customs which make England so splendid.

A Noble Animal

Kindness to Animals

Animals matter more than people because they can't talk. They matter infinitely more than dumb people, but nobody knows why that is.

A beggar's dog moves us much more than his hungry wife and five children, but then it must be remembered that we see the dog whereas he has left his family at home. Would it be equally moving if he had a placard saying, " Six starving dogs to support," without exhibiting them ? We fancy it would not be without effect.

It is very nice and reassuring to reflect that a man who would not risk his life to save a child would be considered quite as much of a cad as a man who would not risk his life to save an animal. There equality ceases.

86

Animals are extraordinarily clever, and intelligent, but this does not count against them because it is in a rather British instinctive way, and—even if they don't exactly muddle through —they don't talk about it. Besides it is character that counts, and there horses and dogs and Englishmen go right up to the top of the class together.

Killing animals if it is not done for profit, self-defence or anger is splendid. It shows your deep interest in animals, it improves hounds and horses, it develops character, and foxes like it. This puts foxes in a class by themselves, because though hares and birds don't mind being chased and shot it is not known if they would actually choose it (see Sport). Anyway, animals are topping little sportsmen. Bull fighting is barbarous.

The Friend of Man

The Stately Mental Homes of England

English Country Houses

English country houses are very beautiful and very moving, and characteristic to such an extent that there is a confused idea that other countries only have Castles.

The English country houses are doomed because the old families cannot afford to keep them up. Those that are not pulled down are either inhabited by parvenus who do not know What is What, or else have become girls' schools or lunatic asylums (see the Famous Houses of London).

The thing about English country houses is that they are very good and full of good things, but never never antagonise you by being in Faultless Good Taste.

G. B. Shaw

Years ago Bernard Shaw had a red beard and was dangerous, fanatic, ungentlemanly, Socialistic and silly. He was a Charlatan. Now he has a white beard and is brilliant, witty and delightful. He is Almost A Classic. He is a vegetarian and is often photographed in a bathing suit and he writes plays; but these facts are incidental—the great thing is to live to be eighty.

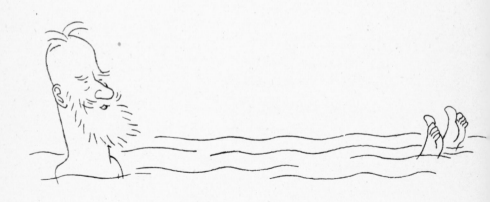

G. B. S.

The Best in the World

You do not need to have travelled, or to have considered any alternative, or to have had the slightest truck with foreigners to know that almost everything British is the best in the world.

Such is our splendid accuracy and sense of justice that it is known that British cooking and climate are not the best in the world. The only other thing is heavy-weight boxers.

The English Sunday

The English Sunday is quite awful and everything is shut and you can't do anything, but it's rather nice and characteristic because no other country would put up with such a thing, and it's one of those things like fog that really impress foreigners, and one of those things like sportsmanship that foreigners cannot really understand.

Unfair Foreign Competition

Foreign competition is unfair. For foreigners to sell anything in England cheaper than the English sell it there, is unfair. They probably do it by sweated labour, injustice, oppression and a cruelly low standard of living. On the other hand it is better not to look too closely into their methods of production, in case there is not so much wrong with it after all. This would make it less unfair, and it has to be unfair anyway.

WHAT YOU KNOW
WHAT YOU DON'T KNOW
ART

What You Know

You've taken your umbrella so of course it won't rain.

Books make the best furniture for a room.

How small the world is.

If you put that in a book people would say it was overdone.

. . . but you do know what you like (see What You Don't Know).

It isn't so much what he says as the way he says it.

A horse when you see one.

What You Don't Know

Much about Art, but . . .(see What You Know).

Where you would be without your wonderful sense of humour.

Art

Coming to the end, we notice that nothing has been said about any form of Art in England. But does this matter ?

IRELAND

INTRODUCTION

Time was when Ireland would have needed all too little introduction. Time was when it was a subject that cropped up everywhere invariably exploding fireworks. Ireland points the sad moral to exhibitionists that you can make too much of a good gesture.

Ireland—actuated no doubt by the purest motives—devoted an infinity of time and trouble to the cause of bothering England. It culminated in her repudiating England and cutting herself off from her with a bang. Whereat England, instantly and to the surprise of all, ceased to mind. The cause (see Oxford) was lost.

The Dictator

Wrongs, Tenacity of Memory, and Oliver Cromwell

The Irish have had a great many wrongs inflicted upon them by the English, partly due to iniquity on one or the other or both sides, but largely due to the English not understanding them. For the Irish have this unique distinction that the English not only do not but can not understand them.

The Irish have remarkable tenacity of memory and cherish their wrongs not only because they are keen wrong-fanciers but because they just do by nature go on remembering wrongs way back in history with the same freshness as though they had happened yesterday. The English have hardly any historical memory at all and cannot bother much about wrongs either received or given unless very recently. This raises a barrier between the English and the Irish, and is due to the fact that though Muddle is a cherished Irish feature and characteristic they have never wished or endeavoured to muddle THROUGH.

The Irish have not yet got through Oliver Cromwell.

Trouble

The Irish are Celtic which makes them dynamic and restless so that they cannot really be expected to settle down to anything so Anglo-Saxon and bovine as peace and contentment and prosperity. The Irish therefore require trouble, and their will-power and personality always amply provide it.

Murder, arson, massacre, pillage, boycotting and torture are handily grouped together under the heading " trouble." A fair judgment.

Charm

Irish charm is one of the really established facts of the world. It is partly due to the voices of the Irish which are delightful and frequently brogues; and partly to the quaint turns of speech such as calling you " your honour " or saying you have " drink taken "; and partly to flattery too obvious for you to believe but not in the least servile or oily because of being blarney; and partly to lying so pointlessly that it is quite disinterested and almost poetic. When they lie as they constantly do to further their own ends and to deceive you it is not exactly charm, but it remains charming.

Inefficiency

The aim of English inefficiency is that things should get done without anyone seeming to care. The aim, gloriously realised, of Irish inefficiency is that things should not get done at all.

Folk Lore

Irish folk lore is very Celtic and romantic and dim and sad, and as poetic as anything. They have Leprechauns who are little old men with beards and crocks of gold; and goodness only knows why a rabble of miserly dwarfs (bearded) should be a score for anyone, but Celts think they are. They have Whitehanded someone and Deirdre of the How-many-is-it Sorrows and a lot of uncharted keening and some unfortunate heroic royal personages, and it is all as sorrowful and mysterious and twilit as anyone could wish it to be. The Irish can often see things and have a lot of soul. The English, who do not hold with anything of the kind at home, quite respect it in the Irish.

" Top o' the mornin' to you, Mr. Kelly! "

Absentee Landlords

In old days landlords in Ireland were frequently absent. This naturally angered the Irish as it restricted the national sport of shooting landlords from behind hedges.

It is not known if there are now any landlords in Ireland.

Dirt and Insanitation

Dirt and insanitation cannot be dismissed as the tribute the Irish pay to their ideal of inefficiency, because it is not as though they aimed at cleanliness and sanitation in the first place. It may possibly be a delicate compliment to the Gentleman Who Pays the Rent as they quaintly call the Pig; because the Pig lives in the parlour or kitchen along with the family. If this is indeed the cause, then the ideal of Irish inefficiency has some bearing after all, because it is well known that by preference and nature and if given a fair chance the Pig is an extraordinarily clean animal and only Man is Vile. The tribute then makes perfect logic, because the Irish have beautiful manners but are not kind even to animals.

G. B. Shaw

(See English Institutions)

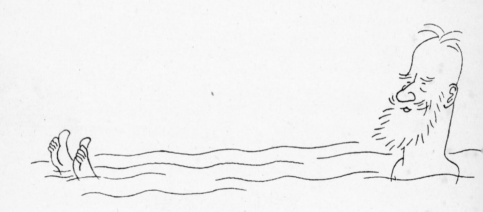

G. B. S.

Hunting and Racing
and the Horse Show

The Irish have a very special kind of relationship with the horse. They are not of course kind to horses. It is more as with the Hungarians, that they know a horse when they see one. Indeed they are very like the Hungarians altogether, what with having such good manners and being so savage underneath and having all those wrongs and charm.

You can get the most beautiful horses in Ireland and you used to be able to get them very cheap. Hunting is very good and democratic and sporting and cheap and a great score. Racing in Ireland is very special and has great Irish cachet, but it is not apparent why; it is not, for instance, particularly inefficient; perhaps it is particularly dirty? The Horse Show is at Dublin and is a thremendous thing and all. It is the high spot of the Irish season.

For anything in connection with horses it is rather knowing to go to Ireland.

Irish America

American Policemen

Owing to difficulties about the Wearing of the Green any quantity of Irish set sail (definitely not in the *Mayflower*) for America. The Irish are terrific fighters and love nothing better than any kind of scrap, so they might well have been tempted to become gangsters. However, the gangsters of America were in such force and had everything so much their own way that any cissy might have thought of being one, so the Irishmen became policemen instead. Or it may have been due to their natural perversity, or because they didn't talk Italian. In any case they had and have to fight incessantly and they still make splendid policemen.

Oddly enough American policemen don't wear the green.

SCOTLAND

INTRODUCTION

The over-intelligent reader may ask himself, what is the meaning of the large sub-section headed History. He may ask: " Why should Scotland have history when England's is not admitted ? If the Bruce, why not Henry VIII ? If Mary Stuart, why not William the Conqueror ? " But the not too intelligent or average reader will probably pass this without comment. Because without thinking it out he will instinctively feel as we do that Scotch history *counts* while English is merely history. The Scotch are so assertive; they are so personal. Mary Stuart and Flora Macdonald get splashed about all over the place instead of retiring into the decent obscurity of Little Arthur.

It is not our personal taste, we are simply recorders. We are set here with clenched teeth and grim jaws to do our duty and to write down What Is Known. And as much Scotch History as follows is Known. It is not our business to say that we think this a pity.

HISTORY

Bonnie Prince Charlie

Bonnie Prince Charlie

Bonnie Prince Charlie was a young pretender. What he pretended was that he was the rightful heir to the throne. Which indeed he was. Only he was a Stuart and they had got invalidated for being Papists. Bonnie P.C. was not a Papist.

The Scotch (probably even then affectedly calling themselves the Scots) people all rallied round B. Prince Charlie, or, properly speaking Chairlie. Even the English, who know that they themselves were right to rally round King George upon his throne because he was a Whig and German and it was pudding time, know that this was very right and loyal and romantic of the Scotch or Scots people. The reason of this is because of lost causes. (See Oxford.)

Chairlie was a young chevalier, and gallant in every sense and pronunciation of the word. He was beloved. He fought all over the place until he reached Derby, when he left for the continent and became the King over the Water. Will he no come back again? He drank a good deal and liked the girls.

"Up we go!"

Mary Stuart

Mary Stuart was beloved, beautiful and romantic to a degree that is almost suffocating. She was pre-eminently a Papist and very notably a Stuart. All these peculiarities are only equalled by the extent to which she was unfortunate. What and how lost a cause ! She liked the French. She was Mary Queen of Scots, and this is rather a score for the Scotch because nowhere in England has anyone been able to suggest that she was Mary Queen of the Scotch.

Mary Stuart got involved in several marriages. She has been a good deal reviled for blowing up one of her husbands (in the literal and final sense) while he was suffering from smallpox, it being generally felt that it would have been better sportsmanship to kill him when he was feeling more keen on life.

It is known that she had four Marys, called Mary Beaton, Mary Seaton, Mary Carmichael and me. It is also known that she hadn't.

Rob Roy

Rob Roy was tremendously Scotch. Sir Walter Scott wrote a long novel about him.

The Wallace

The Wallace was a Warrior-King. He fought the English.

The Bruce

The Bruce was a Warrior-King. He fought the English.

The Spider

The Spider wasn't. It didn't.

The Douglas

Douglas, Douglas, tender and true.

The Douglas was a great hero. He had a Bleeding Heart. He was black.

False Argyll

It is not known for certain whether he was only one man, or whether there was always one of these around at any period. In any case, there was only one at a time. He was a Campbell so, of course, everyone else hated him. One nice thing about him was that he was a Duke.

Battles and Massacres

Battles were fought with the English and Massacres with other Scotch.

The Scotch are extraordinarily battle- and massacre-conscious.

Clans

There are a great many of these and they are all at bitter enmity and have sworn blood feuds. The only clan about which one really universal piece of information is disseminated is the Campbells.

GEOGRAPHY

Highlands and Lowlands

The Highlands are very reasonably higher than the Lowlands. They are wilder and more inaccessible and heatherier and more haunted by men in kilts. They are really Better and More Romantic, although a persevering number of authors such as Sir Walter Scott and Stevenson and Andrew Lang and John Buchan have fair danged away at the Lowlands trying to bolster them up. All the same, the impression remains that Lowlanders are fatter and more prosperous and don't wear kilts, and talk a different and inferior brand of Scotch.

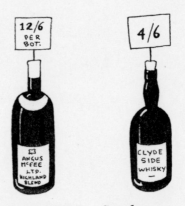

Inferior Scotch

Edinburgh

Edinburgh is the capital and has Holyrood (of course not Hollywood) and is beautiful and has a war memorial and definitely a castle. It is possible that it is one of the hundred best places that may be called the Athens of the North. That would be optional; what is obligatory is that it is one of the few places that absolutely may not be called the Venice of the North on any account.

Perth

The Scotch call it Pai-r-r-th and it had a fair maid.

Aberdeen

A great weariness falls on the spirit when confronted with this paragraph. The Aberdonians are Mean, but they are really very generous and spend all their time making up funny stories about their own meanness. It would really be better if they were quite simply mean.

Glasgow

Glasgow has slums and shipbuilding and slums.

Paisley

Paisley has shawls. Its people are pre-eminently bodies.

Peebles

The name Peebles is almost synonymous with the word Plee-sure.

Dundee

Dundee has marmalade and its bonnets are up.

LITERATURE

Songs

Songs were about Chairlie.

Ballads

Ballads were about blood or bluid.

Sir Walter Scott

Sir Walter Scott was a gentleman. Sir Walter Scott was nice. He wrote a great deal.

Burns

Robbie or Bobby Burns was partial to mice.

CHARACTERISTICS

"fairthermoor —"

Meanness

(See Aberdeen.)

Boringness

The Scotch talk very slowly and literally and at enormous length with the irresistible momentum of tanks, and all in dialect.

Superiority

As the English know their superiority to the Continent, so do the Scotch know their superiority to the English. Such certainty always commands belief. That is what superiority is.

Lack of Humour

The Scotch have no sense of humour to such a portentous and awful extent that instead of being a ridiculous disqualification it becomes a positive power, a sombre splendour. Nothing illustrates so strongly the inhumanness of the Scotch; the great English virtue that has made us top nation and for lack of which the continent is invalidated and eats frogs, the need of Brazilians and Esquimaux, the hope of the world, has simply no application to Scotland at all.

Dourness

The Scotch are very rude, disagreeable, gruff, silent, emotionally inhibited, secretive and unenthusiastic. There is something rather solid and admirable about all this. It is proved by their alluding to English people who try to be polite and conversational and draw them out as Sassenachs. This is a score for Scotland.

Success

Every post of any importance in England or the Empire is held by a Scotchman too comparatively insignificant to rise at home. Even the Jews pay them the graceful tribute of a ruling that ambitious Jewish money-lenders should take Scotch names.

Humour

We are very sorry to be obliged to state that Scotch humour is " pawky." But what can one do ?

Generosity

(See Aberdeen.)

133

"For the sake of auld lang syne"

Whisky Drinking

Whisky is the Scotch national drink and consequently cotters, crofters, etcetera fall into the burn on their way home from a funeral. It is spelt without an e or else it would be Irish, they drink it raw and in enormous quantities which is curiously very splendid, and unescapably they call it " Whusky." On the other hand the good stuff is known all over the world as Scotch, and this is a score for the English as not a single Scotchman has ever been able to suggest that the proper name for it is Scots.

Burns

Bobby or Robbie Burns is Scotland's top and almost only poet.

Porridge

Porridge is supped standing and with salt, and it isn't " it " at all it's " them." These are all terrific scores for the Scotch.

Haggis

Haggis is a kind of sacred boiled pudding made of insides. There are a lot of jokes about it and how horrifying it is, but some English try to like it because of the dominatingness of the Scotch.

Pipes

It is possible that it is the pipes that have made Scotland what it is. There are a great many jokes about them, but all rather dreary, and consisting largely of conjecturing that it is really the pig being killed. It is perhaps going a little far to play the pipes round and round the dining-room table at meal times, but otherwise they are quite justly a score for the Scotch.

Highland
Games

Braemar Brawn

K<small>M</small>

Highland Games

Brawny men perform obscure manœuvres, such as putting the stone and tossing the caber. Horrid little girls in corkscrew ringlets and medals dance Highland flings. There is any amount of fancy dress and a great skirling of pipes. It is bitterly cold and rains all the time. This is the high spot of the Scotch season.

Flora Macdonald

Flora Macdonald is inextricably mixed up with Chairlie. This is not only very commendable but it is, so far as we know, not scandalous at all because, so far as we know, we don't mean what you mean. She was brave and very romantic and is one of those things that have made Douglas Byng what he is.

Presbyterianism

Two things are known about Presbyterianism, or the Scotch religion; it is exceedingly dour and the dogs go to church. In view of the second qualification it is hard to understand why it is not the religion of England; especially as the first characteristic, though equally salient, may be less fundamental because the Scotch are dour anyway. The probable reason is that as our religion is called Church of England it is only sense that we should have that. And then, the Scotch have no Bishops. Besides, do dogs like church ?

The Highland Meetings

The Highland Meetings take place at Oban and that sort of thing. They mean dances (for which of course it is essential to meet). They are tremendously Scotland-Conscious.

"So you won't talk, huh?"

Sport

The Scotch season is in August and September because of Sport.

Sport consists largely of shooting. Not landlords, as in Ireland, but birds. Scotch landowners let their shooting to stockbrokers from London, and to Birmingham boot manufacturers, and still more and overpoweringly to Americans. These all cut figures of fun because of Scotch National Dress (see Scotch National Dress) and ghillies which are still more difficult.

Ghillies are a sort of personification of mortification to others. They know everything about nature and sport and always notice that you are always wrong. They are dour. They talk very little, and when they do it's in dialect, but whether you understand it or not you can tell it's unpleasant. You always feel apologetic. How they look down on you. You have to have them.

Fishing gets left over into the season from the fishing season which is earlier. What you fish for is fush. These are salmon.

Stalking takes all day and is very strenuous. What you are actually stalking is a stag, but it wouldn't matter if you didn't know, as you probably wouldn't get the chance of a shot at one anyway. It's a very superior sport.

Pride

The Scotch take offence.

In tipping the lower classes, there you are between their pride and their avarice.

How you will mind doing the wrong thing.

Golf

Golf is the Scotch National Game. Do not confuse it with the Highland Games. It is Royal and Ancient. It takes place at St. Andrews and Gleneagles. Caddies come out rather as juvenile second-rate ghillies, but they are perter and less dour.

National Dress

Every other nation in Europe has many varieties of people who wear different kinds of national dress quite unself-consciously all the time, but in Britain there is only Scotland—and even there the Scotch mostly don't dress up. But many quite otherwise staid and sober Englishmen cannot be prevented from clothing themselves in Scotch National Costume. It consists of a short pleated petticoat coming down to the knees and a long trailing sort of shawl affixed to the left shoulder. These are made of violently patterned woollen stuff. A little furry pouch is slung across the stomach and a knife is worn stuck in the stocking. Two funny kinds of little bonnet complete the outfit. It is a great privilege to have the right to wear this get-up.

PERSONALITIES

Sir Harry Lauder

Sir Harry Lauder invented singing Scotch songs not about Chairlie.

Sir James Barrie

Sir James Barrie discovered Mothers and Fairies.

INSTITUTIONS

Bonnie Prince Charlie

Chairlie is your darling.

Success

The Scotch succeed.

Burns

Brobbie Burns is Sacred. He was always drunk.

NOBODIES & SOMEBODIES

Doris Orgel

NOBODIES

& SOMEBODIES

Viking

Acknowledgements

I want to thank Esther Adler, Sophia Appel, Natalie Brinton, Kathryn Callaghan, Jessica Cordina, Pauline DeTrabue, Rebecca Ellin, Zoraya Garces, Kei Hoshino, Gretchen Lustig, Jennifer Macken, Melisande Mond, Dinanga Mulumba, Khartoon Ohan, Tulay Onay, Alexandra Rigney, Sonia Van Dyne and Marcia Yablon. Back when they were fifth-graders, we had some good talks, and I'm grateful that they trusted me with their feelings about the whys, why nots, and ins and outs of clubs. Many thanks also to Ms. Dorothy Donovan, their teacher, for making our talks possible.

VIKING
Published by the Penguin Group
Viking Penguin, a division of Penguin Books USA Inc.,
375 Hudson Street, New York, New York 10014, U.S.A.
Penguin Books Ltd, 27 Wrights Lane, London W8 5TZ, England
Penguin Books Australia Ltd, Ringwood, Victoria, Australia
Penguin Books Canada Ltd, 10 Alcorn Avenue, Toronto,
Ontario, Canada M4V 3B2
Penguin Books (N.Z.) Ltd, 182–190 Wairau Road, Auckland 10, New Zealand
Penguin Books Ltd, Registered Offices: Harmondsworth, Middlesex, England
First published in 1991 by Viking Penguin, a division of
Penguin Books USA Inc.

1   3   5   7   9   10   8   6   4   2

Copyright © Doris Orgel, 1991
All rights reserved
Library of Congress Catalog Card Number: 90-51002
ISBN 0-670-82754-1

Printed in the U.S.A.
Set in 13 point Garamond #3

For Regina

$\mathcal{L}$aura Hoffman

The first thing I saw when I walked into Room 309 were three girls sitting on the windowsill, looking like they owned the place. They were a club—*the* club. It was written all over their faces.

Great. I was new, I didn't know a soul. One look at them and I felt even more like Ms. Nobody from Noplace.

We'd just moved here. This was my first Monday morning in Gifford.

The morning had started off with a *crash*. I was just leaving the house. There was this pond behind it. And Max, our dog, fell through the ice.

I nearly fell in myself, dragging him out of there. He shivered and shook, like he'd never warm up. He gave me this reproachful look: What kind of place is this, anyway?

"You poor guy." I hugged him. That got me even more drenched. I went and changed to other jeans and my favorite old blue sweater with bears on it. I'd wanted to wear that in the first place, but my sister Mary Lou said it looked stupid.

Mary Lou was more into clothes than I was. Clothes did more for her, too. That was so unfair, since she got all the looks in the first place. Personality, too, everything.

She'd already left for her new school, Gifford High. She'd gotten a ride with Dad. And I bet that by lunch time, maybe sooner, she'd already have a dozen friends, all the popular kids in her class.

When I got back downstairs, Mom was up on the stepladder. We were still not all unpacked, and she was putting kitchen stuff away. "Want me to drive you?" she asked.

I was due at Ludcomb Middle School at ten of nine. I still had twenty minutes and it wasn't that far. So I said, "That's okay, Mom, I'll walk."

I should have let her. I was the only kid walking alone. I got into the deep dumps, and I wished I was back in Tuscola.

Then, when I was hanging up my stuff in the closet, this girl with a round face and red-rimmed glasses came and hung hers up on the next peg. She had thick black hair. She wore it in a ponytail. She gave me this please-like-me smile. And I thought she was going to ask who I was, etc. But she stuttered and could only get out "Um, uh—?"

I had a friend back in Tuscola, Rusty. She stuttered. She was so amazing, though. She made it seem like something special. She'd quote you the latest figures on how rare this was among girls. Or she'd tell you that Julius Caesar, or Shakespeare, or someone like that stuttered as a kid. And whether it was true or not, you liked her just the same. She was smart and funny. Sometimes it took her forever just saying, Hi, how're you doing? But if you hung in there and waited it out, she could talk your ear off.

I said, "Hi, I'm Laura Hoffman. We just moved here."

She had a big struggle getting her name said. Janet Di Chocolate, or something. After that her stutter let up. I guess she could tell that I didn't think it was a big deal. "Where did you move from?" she asked.

"Tuscola, Illinois. My father works for Hammond Electronics. They made him transfer here."

"Oh. Well, I've lived here my whole life. And Gifford's okay, you'll like it. Ludcomb's okay too, so's Ms. Tatum, so are the kids in this class—"

Kick, kick, kick, the girls on the windowsill were drumming their heels against the wall, all together, in rhythm. Janet shot them a poison look and said, "Except them. Those three are not okay."

Their sneakers were the "in" brand, I knew, because my sister had two pairs of the same kind. Their knock-'em-dead outfits were new, in con-

5

trasting coordinated colors—raspberry pink, grape-jelly purple, kelly green—like they'd shopped for them together. The girl in pink had a frowzy-haired face on her shirt. It was a woman with her mouth wide open, a singer, somebody famous; I knew who, but I just couldn't think of her name.

That girl whispered something to the one in purple who passed it on to the one in green. And they all giggled.

"Oh, ha, ha," went Janet.

I said, "They're a club, aren't they?"

"Right. They're the Supes."

"You mean like tomato? Chicken noodle?"

"No. Like in 'super.'" She told me their names. "Liz Faber, Beth Henderson, Vero Jencks-Norris."

"Which is which?"

"Liz is the one with that face on her shirt. She's the leader. Next to her's Beth. She's always next to Liz. She can't stand it when she's not. The last one down is Vero."

"Vero? With an o?"

"Yeah."

"Is 'Supers' the name of their club?"

"No. 'Super Stars.' Modest, right? That was their club last year, before Vero; she only moved here last fall."

"What's their club called now?"

"Um—" Janet flushed. Like she knew. But she didn't say.

"What makes them so super superior?"

"I don't know. I guess that they think so. Their clothes, being rich and all. And special things they do."

"Like what?"

"Liz does ballet, she's good. Beth does gymnastics. And did you ever see 'Jet Away With Ted and Kay,' that travel show that sometimes comes on after the news? Those are Beth's parents. And Vero—" Ms. Tatum came in just then. Janet's voice dropped to a whisper. "Vero swims with dolphins," I thought Janet said.

Ms. Tatum was old, around fifty, and tall, with big teeth, a bony chin, kind of horsy looking. She had a nice smile, though. I'd already met her on Friday when I came to get registered.

Janet said, "Hey, Laura, want to sit at our table? There's room. It's the one over there. Want to ask Ms. Tatum if you can?"

Ms. Tatum was yelling at the "Supes" to get down off the windowsill. I waited till she was done. Then I went up to her and asked. She said, "Fine."

It was really two tables put together like a T. Most of the tables in this room were like that. The other kids at it were Cory Soong, a skinny, dark-haired girl with bangs, a boy with a brush **7** cut, and another boy with straw-colored hair.

Janet and Cory were great to me all morning, showed me where to get my books, what place we were up to, how to head my work sheets.

At lunch they saved me a seat at their table. And I met their friends from the other fifth grade, Julie Holmar and Shawna Murtrie.

Then it was recess. There I was, with the four of them, playing Spuds! When I'd expected I would still not know anybody and would have to hang around by myself.

After Spuds they went and sat on the playground steps. That was their jacks territory. They took out their jacks and flipped. Janet and Shawna got first turn.

Janet's fingers moved like whirlwinds. She beat Shawna easily. Julie and Cory played next. They were all really good. Then Janet asked, "Are you ready, Laura? 'Cause you're next."

"No thanks, you'd beat me by a mile." I hadn't played since third grade. After that, kids in Tuscola didn't go in for jacks very much. "I wouldn't be any competition for you. Hey, look!"

Beth was doing a turn-around on the climbing bars, hanging by her knees from the next-to-the-top bar.

A man teacher on recess duty rushed over there, yelling, "Cut that out, you'll break your neck!"

Beth turned right side up and joined Liz and Vero. The three of them sat on top of there, like it was their throne to look down on everybody from.

The weather was windy and raw. The sky'd been gray the whole morning. Now the clouds started blowing apart, and the sun came out. The Supes tipped their heads back to get sunshine on their faces. Liz unzipped her parka. The sun lit up the face on her shirt as bright as with a spotlight. And the name of that singer popped back into my mind—Glenda Tyrone. How could I've forgotten? Mary Lou was a big fan of hers. She'd bought her new single the day it hit the stores.

I thought, What am I doing, sitting on these steps, watching a jacks game? And I don't know what came over me. I mean, I was so not their type! But I felt like something was pulling me toward the climbing bars.

"Hey Laura, where're you going?" called Janet. "Don't, you're wasting your time!"

———————

"Stop!" called Liz.

I'd only gotten to the second climbing bar. "I just want to tell you something."

"What about?"

"Your shirt."

"Tell me from down there. What about my shirt?"

"Just, I like it." And I said—even though it was more Mary Lou's opinion than mine— "Glenda Tyrone is terrific."

They went "What?" and "Huh?" Like they couldn't believe their ears. "Say that again?"

"That singer on your shirt, Glenda Tyrone, is terrific."

Liz and Beth locked eyes. Then they looked at Vero like whatever'd just happened was her fault.

"*I* didn't tell her," said Vero.

I asked, "Tell me what?"

Liz glared at me. She had light gray eyes. They shone like aluminum. "None of your business!"

What secret had I stumbled onto? I was dying to know. I said the magic words again, "Glenda Tyrone is terrific," just to see what would happen.

Same surprised, suspicious looks.

Beth asked, "Who told you? Come on, tell."

"No one told me anything, honest. What's this all about?"

"It's about that you said our password," said Liz in a frozen voice. "At least it *was* our password. Now we'll have to get a new one."

I said—I don't know where I got the

nerve—"Maybe it just means that I should be in your club."

Who, you? They didn't have to say it. They looked me over—Liz and Beth did, anyway. Here's what they saw: A skinny girl, mousy brown hair, no figure yet, wearing a too-big parka (an old one of Mary Lou's, because mine got all wet), baggy jeans, no-name sneakers.

Vero smiled. Kind of, anyway. She had green eyes, freckles, curly reddish hair. I started liking her. That sometimes happens, before you even know a person. And I wanted to be friends with her.

She whispered something in Beth's ear. Beth whispered it to Liz. They argued back and forth, about what to do about me.

Then they asked me my whole life history. Where was I from? What was it like there? Who were my friends? What clubs had I ever been in? Was I good at obeying rules? Keeping secrets? And, was there anything special that I knew how to do that they didn't? Liz asked me that like she doubted it very much.

Hm. I doubted it, too. "Well, when we first got our dog I helped house train him. So I know how to do that."

"It's not exactly the kind of thing we had in mind," said Beth.

11

"Anything else?" Liz looked at her Swatch, like, Don't take all day.

I doubted that this would count either, but I couldn't come up with anything better. "How about rescuing dogs? Ours fell through the ice, and I pulled him out."

"What ice?" asked Beth. "Bishop's Pond? Do you live near it?"

"Yes, it's right behind our house."

"It is? If we gave you a task, just to see if you're worthy, would you do it?" asked Liz.

"What kind of task?"

"Never mind." Like, I'd blown it, just by asking that.

So I said, "All right, I'd do it."

"Okay. But first you have to swear not to tell our password to anyone. Swear, by something you hold dear."

"All right, I swear."

"You may climb up," said Liz.

I started to. I thought, Not bad for my first day at Ludcomb. I wished Mary Lou could see me. I got to the fourth climbing bar. Then— wouldn't you know?—the bell rang, and we had to go inside.

What task would they give me? Then would I be in, if I did it okay? That was all I could think about the whole rest of the school day.

12   At ten of three the bell rang for the walk-

ers to line up. I got on line behind Janet. She ignored me, only talked to Cory. Since recess they'd been acting like I'd gone over to the enemy.

Janet went "Brrr," when we got outside. She was excited about how cold it had gotten. "It feels like it's only twenty degrees!" She forgot about staying mad at me, grabbed my arm, "Want to know a shortcut to your house? Come on!"

We crossed to the far end of the playground, and took a dirt path from there. "Wait till you see where this goes!"

It led through a field of dried-out stubble, then through woods a short distance, and there was the pond, right in front of us! I hadn't realized it curved around this way. It was frozen solid. People were on it, skating.

Janet pointed straight across. "See over there? That's Pebble Brook Road."

I said, "Great, there's our house, the white one with the deck near those pine trees."

Janet lived near the narrow end of the pond, in the opposite direction. But she'd been so nice to show me the shortcut, I said, "Want me to walk you part way?"

"Okay, if you want to."

First we were quiet. After awhile she said, "Don't get your hopes up. I mean about the Supes. They're just stringing you along."

"Why do you think that?"

"I just do. Don't ask." She changed the subject. "Do you like to skate?"

"Yes, do you?"

"Yes. Want to skate together, later?"

"Sure, if my skates aren't still packed."

"Well, call me up." She told me her number. "If you don't remember it, it's in the phone book, under Alan Di Ciocchio." She spelled it.

"Okay, I will. See you later, I hope."

"Yeah, me too. So long."

———————

When I got near our house, Max came running and jumped all over me, nearly knocking me down.

Mom was in the mud room. She'd put up a peg board. My skates were hanging from it. "Mom, great, you found my skates!"

"How was school?"

"Fine, I'll tell you later. Can I go skating?"

"I don't see why not."

"Terrific, I'll go change." I ran upstairs.

"Mary Lou has a friend over," Mom called after me.

Mary Lou and I shared a room, like in our old house. It could be a pain. Like, we had this rule that whoever had company, the other cleared

out. But at night it felt good knowing she was

in the next bed. And we had good talks, some-times. Like, we could say things to each other just before we went to sleep that we couldn't, other times.

Anyway, she and this other girl were on the floor, leaning on their elbows, chomping on trail mix, writing numbers on a chart. Mary Lou put her arm over it, but I'd already seen. It was a rating chart of boys in their class.

"Stacey, this is my kid sister. Laura, this is Stacey Kimball. There's more trail mix down-stairs." Subtle hint.

"Hi, Stacey, pleased to meet you. I'll just be a sec." I ducked into the closet, put on thick jeans and my skating sweater.

Then I went into Mom and Dad's room to call Janet. While I was looking up her number, the phone rang.

In our family, when the phone rings, nine times out of ten it's for Mary Lou. But this time it was for me. It was Liz, asking, "Can we come over?"

"Sure!"

I ran downstairs. "Mom, I'm having company, too, these girls from my class are coming over, okay?"

"Fine." Mom was pleased for me.

I had to shut Max in the garage, or he'd jump all over them. "Just for a little while, sorry." **15**

Then I got out cider, soda, cupcakes, cookies, every snackable thing we had.

They came in a cream-color Saab. They had their skates around their necks. Liz and Beth wore skating outfits. Vero, jeans and her parka.

They didn't want snacks. We put our skates on right away. They thought it was neat how our deck led straight out onto the pond.

The three of them linked arms, Liz in the middle. Where did that leave me?

Vero held out her free arm, "Come on, Laura!"

The ice was smooth as glass. The wind blew from behind us, and we glided forward easily. Everything looked beautiful, the trees and houses along the shore, black crows and white sea gulls in the sky, ribbon-y clouds turning pink in the west, like a picture of a perfect afternoon. It was great. I felt terrific.

We came to an inlet where people figure-skated. "Watch this!" Liz did a twirl.

"Watch *this*!" Beth did a figure eight.

Vero and I were the cheering section. Then Vero said, "My toes are getting cold. I want to skate some more."

I said, "Me too."

"If you guys want to practice more, we'll see you later," Vero said.

We skated on. She told me she'd learned how **16** that winter. In Florida, where she came from, it never got that cold. Then she asked, "What's your dog's name? What kind is he?"

"Max. He's a black and gray Lab."

"Those are big, aren't they? You must have had some job pulling him out of the pond. Can I see him when we get back to your house?"

"Sure. Now can I ask you something?"

"Sure."

"Janet said you swam with dolphins."

We were skating along pretty fast. She said, "So?"

"So, I was just wondering, what was it like?"

"I can't describe it, you have to do it, that's the only way you can know."

"I saw it on TV. You know that show *Dolphin Cove*, about a girl who's friends with dolphins someplace in Australia—?"

"It's not like on TV," she said. Then she bent her knees for speed and shot away.

I finally caught up to her back at the figure-skating inlet. I said, "Whew, you're fast."

She didn't say a word.

"Now do you want to see Max?" I asked when we got back to my house.

She shrugged. Like she'd never even asked to.

"Thanks for letting us change here," said Liz. They put their sneakers back on, cleaned off their skate blades, hung their skates around their necks.

Liz said, "Here comes Mrs. Fogarty." The Fabers' housekeeper drove up in the Saab. They hopped in. " 'Bye, Laura."

I let Max out of the garage. He ran and joined other dogs on the ice.

When I went back in the kitchen, Mom was standing at the oven basting a chicken. "Well? Was it fun with those girls?"

"It was okay."

"Just okay?" She turned around to me. "What went wrong?"

"Nothing, Mom." I didn't want to start complaining. We'd promised we wouldn't, back in Tuscola, when Dad first told us about getting transferred.

We'd been eating dinner. Dad hadn't touched his food. He was really upset. He said, "They've reorganized the company in such a way, there'll be no more work for me here. I *have* to go to Gifford, or I'll be out of a job. I know how hard it'll be on you girls. And on you, Cath." (Mom). He came up with the idea of him moving first, by himself. That way, Mom could train someone to take her job (she was the medical technician in a doctor's office). And that way, Mary Lou and I could finish the school year. "I'd do fine on my own for a short while," he said, with this forced smile. He looked miserable.

18   "From February till June, a *short* while?" Mom

went over to him and rumpled his hair. "Forget it!" She laid her head in the crook of his neck. They usually didn't do those things in front of us. We weren't the kind of family that said emotional stuff out loud very often. But she said, "Our family being together is what matters the most. Mary Lou and Laura, do you agree?"

Yes. We voted. It was unanimous, we'd all move together. Then, to cheer up Dad, we wrote this "resolution" in curlicue script on the chalkboard in our family room:

"Resolved: To be good sports, no bellyaching, no feeling sorry for ourselves, etc."

So now Mom said, "It's okay, belly-ache to me."

So I did. "Oh Mom, I wanted those girls to like me. But they don't. The only reason they came over was to have a place to change."

Mom was getting some wrinkles and a few gray hairs. She'd been working around the house and she looked a mess. But even so, she looked beautiful. And she said this Mom-thing, "What? How could they not like you?"

She pulled me close, so my head was against her chest. "It's just hard, because you're missing your friends back home. Know how I know?"

Yes, of course. She knew from missing *her* friends, that she'd had even longer. I looked in her face. And we both started laughing, because **19** we were both so nearly crying, that it wasn't even funny.

Then Dad got home.

He'd had a good day. His boss here liked how his first project was shaping up. And they'd forwarded his favorite picture from his office in Tuscola, Van Gogh's *Boats,* and he'd hung it in his new office, over his desk. "And I was thinking, in summer we might want to get a boat. And speaking of the pond, guess who I saw, having a good time, skating with no skates on. Max."

"Better than this morning. He fell in." Mom told that I rescued him.

"Good, Laura. Did you skate this afternoon? Was it fun?"

"Yes." Well, it was, part of the time.

At dinner Mary Lou raved about Gifford High. "It's great. They have this drama club, Thespians, and their cheerleading squad got an award in a statewide competition last year."

Dad asked, "Which one will be lucky and get you?"

"Dad, it's not that easy. You have to be interviewed for Thespians, then you have to pre-audition. And for cheerleaders, you don't just go up to them and say, 'Guys, here I am.' It's up to them, they 'tap' you if they want you." Mary

Lou looked down at her plate. She wasn't going

to say it, but we all knew it: She'd be in Thespians and cheerleaders, both. Soon, too.

"And you, Laura? Tell about Ludcomb," Mom said.

"Ludcomb's okay. Please pass the salad?"

Later, when we were in bed, Mary Lou asked, "What got you so down?"

So then it all spilled out. I was sure she'd understand.

Instead, she started in on me, "Why do you want to be in that club?"

"Everyone does. Same reason you want to be in Thespians and cheerleaders."

"It's not the same," she said in her older-and-wiser voice. "As for wanting to be friends with that girl Vera so much—"

"Ver*o*."

"Whatever her name is." Mary Lou turned preachy. "I'll tell you something, Laura. The only way to have friends is to *be* one."

I said, "Thank you, Mrs. Dinkerhoff." She was our ninety-year-old Brownie leader back in Tuscola. "Good night. I'm going to sleep now." I pulled the covers up to my chin.

Then I remembered—I hadn't called Janet!

I felt like a total louse. It was too late to call her now. Besides, what would I say? Sorry, Janet, I forgot, because the Supes were coming over? **21**

Janet Di Ciocchio

••••••••••

I hated the Supes, I hated their club, and everything about them!

My stutter wasn't so bad. I'd probably outgrow it. That's what the speech therapist I went to a couple of times had said.

Well, she didn't hear me talking to that new girl, Laura Hoffman. It was awful. Like my mouth was stuffed with c-c-cotton. I couldn't even say my name.

I figured she'd walk away, or get jittery. Fiddle with her hair, the way Cory did, or chew on her lip, like Shawna. And they were my friends. They should have been used to it!

This girl Laura was like, take my time, fine with her, it didn't bother her one bit. That worked. I wanted to thank her, do her a favor back. I hoped like anything she'd like me.

She started to. But then, like out of the blue, she went over to the Supes.

They hated it when I called them that. So I did it all the more. I hated them so much! They were ruining my whole life!

So then, how come deep down, I wanted to *be* one? I couldn't understand it. But there it was.

22 If they'd so much as nodded in my direction, I'd

have dropped everything, and come running. I'd have done whatever they wanted me to. I hated that about myself. But I couldn't help it.

I stuttered, wore glasses, wasn't exactly thin. I was the least like a Supe you could be. And yet, at the end of last summer—shazam! Or anyway, almost . . .

It was Saturday of Labor Day weekend. Joey and I were out on our porch. Mom was working in the piano room. Dad was out teaching. I was supposed to keep Joey entertained.

"I'll teach you jacks," I offered. But he just kept grabbing the ball away, and bouncing it like crazy so it went all over the place and I had to chase it.

Joey was in love with my jacks ball. It was a beauty, made of clear blue plastic with tiny gold and silver stars inside. I think he thought its blueness came from the real sky, its stars from the real stars, and that it was magic.

He was too young to learn jacks. I gave up. "Okay, we'll play Cars." That was more his type of game. You guessed what make and color car would come down our hill next.

"A Chevy," Joey guessed, "no, a Datsun, blue, no, green."

"No fair changing your mind. Which?"

"Datsun, red."

Wrong—a Ford Escort, green.

23

Then he said, "I hear a Saab." And, what do you know! A Saab came down our hill. Cream, with a sun roof. Like the Fabers had. I thought, What if it's Liz, just stopping by? And told myself, Dream on!

It *was* the Fabers' car. Out stepped Liz, saying "Hi, Janet," like we were friends.

"Yay, hurray, a Saab, I won, ten points!" Joey yelled and jumped up and down like a fiend.

Liz had some music with her. "You know this big benefit my parents are giving tomorrow? For the Gifford Arts Council? And I'm supposed to dance at it?" She made it all sound like questions, the way people do when they want you to get ready to say yes to something they're about to ask you. "But guess what happened, Mrs. Seidel, my accompanist? She fell down her cellar stairs, and broke her wrist. So now she can't play the piano. And my parents told all their friends I'd dance, and I've practiced so hard, and now I can't, without an accompanist, so I was wondering, Janet, would you—?"

"Yes!" I didn't think the Supes even knew that I played the piano. Besides, if they did, I'd have expected them to think it was nerdy. So I was surprised and thrilled. I asked, "Can I see the music?"

She handed it to me. It was from Tchaikov-sky's Nutcracker Suite. It looked hard. Usually a piece this hard would have taken me a week. But I promised myself I'd learn it by tomorrow, even if I had to stay up the whole night and not get a wink of sleep.

Liz said, "So, do you think one of them could?"

One of who? I was deep into my daydream. It took me a while to catch on: She meant my mom or my dad. Of course. They were professional pianists. All Liz wanted me to do was to take her to them so she could ask them.

I took her down to the piano room. Mom said, sorry, she was accompanying a cellist at a recital tomorrow. She thought Dad might be free, but she wasn't sure. She said, "He'll be back soon."

Liz couldn't wait. The Fabers' housekeeper was honking for her. She said, "You ask him for me, would you, Janet? Tell him to call as soon as he gets back." She got into the Saab, and *vrrrm!*

Dad came home in a little while. He called up the Fabers. Yes, he was free tomorrow, he'd be glad to do it. And Mrs. Faber said to bring me along.

•••••••••••

The Fabers' house was like a mansion. It had pillars and a veranda, which is like a porch, except it's upstairs. Their garden was bigger than our whole street.

25

Liz's parents were more the age of grandparents. They *were* grandparents. They had a grown-up son and daughter who already had kids.

Liz's father had been First Selectman of Gifford a few years back and was on the Town Council. Liz's mother was chairwoman of United Fund. They knew everybody in town. It was a huge party.

They'd put wooden flooring on the front lawn for a grand piano to stand on. There were rows of folding chairs for people to sit on during the performance.

Beth was there, of course. She was not thrilled to see me.

I asked, "Are your parents here?" I was curious to meet them.

"They're in Saint-Tropez," she said, like any idiot would know where that was.

"Oh."

We sat together on the grass in front of the chairs because we both wanted to be up close.

Looking at Liz in her gauzy costume with her glittering wand, you could almost believe there could be such a thing as a sugar-plum fairy. She was fantastic. She moved as though she weighed no more than a feather, as though she were floating on the air.

In the middle of the dance she came whirling over to us and waved her wand—over me! Once, twice . . . I held absolutely still. I wanted her to do it one more time. Of course I didn't believe in magic. Not the way little kids, like Joey, did. Still, three had always been my lucky number. And I got this shivery feeling. Like, if she'd just wave it one more time, I'd be transformed. Changed into somebody different, somebody more like, well, *some*body. I knew it was stupid to feel that way. Her wand was just a piece of wood with glitter pasted on. But still . . . I thought, Do it, come on! And she did.

Dad had to leave right after Liz's dance to go pick up Joey at Grandpa's. But Liz wanted me to stay. Mrs. Faber said they'd bring me home, so Dad said, "Okay."

Liz went inside to change. Beth and I hung around the party. Beth filled up on canapés. Not the new, the transformed me. I was too excited, and besides, I wanted to get thin.

Liz came back out wearing shorts. "Come on, let's go cool off!" She grabbed us by the hands, and we ran to the back of the house, down another big lawn, to a tall, spraying fountain. She pulled off her shorts, her shirt, and yelled, "Last one in is a goop!"

Me, I was the goop. I hugged my arms around my middle, waiting for remarks. But Liz shook her head at Beth, like to say, Let's be nice to her. "Hey, look, I have rainbows on my arms!" **27**

We held our arms out in the spray. We danced, we splashed around. It was wonderful.

When we had our clothes back on, Liz said, "Now let's go in the woods."

"Not too far, though," Beth said. And after awhile, "Hey, this is far enough. We're getting near the you-know."

"So? Listen, Beth, if Janet's father hadn't played the piano for me, I couldn't have done my whole dance. I say, let's show it to her."

"You're crazy," said Beth.

Liz said, "No, I'm not."

Then we were there. At the "you-know." It was a tree house. Not just a shack, like most are, but really nice, built onto a platform high up in a maple tree. It was neatly painted, white, with a green door and green shutters. Ladder steps led to it.

Beth asked, "Are we letting her up?"

"Yes. Relax."

Beth said, "You *are* crazy."

"Don't worry, I know what I'm doing."

We went up the stairs, first Liz, then Beth, then me. A sign on the door said "Super Stars." Liz took it down.

"Hey," Beth protested.

"We need a new name," said Liz.

We went inside. It was roomy with benches along the walls and a round tree stump for a table. It smelled good, a woody smell, and when you looked out the windows you were in a tree world.

I had to pinch myself, like when you're scared it could just be a dream. But it was real. I was in their club house!

"Now that we're here, let's have a meeting," said Liz.

"With *Janet?* Now I know you're crazy," said Beth.

"I told you, relax. We can trust her. Can't we, Janet?"

I said, "Yes."

"And anyway," said Liz, "we'll take out secrets' insurance."

"How?" asked Beth.

"Tell you later. This meeting will now come to order." Liz banged her fist on the table. "First on the agenda, I don't like 'Super Stars' anymore. It's too braggy. Let's think of a new name."

Beth said, "How about 'Terrifics'? Or, how about 'the Tops'?"

"No. Too braggy, too. And blah. We need dazzle. We'll think one up later. Who'll we have for our idol?"

"Cameron." Cameron Fairfax, from the soap everybody was watching, *How the Heart Yearns.* Beth gave a lovesick sigh.

Liz said, "Watch it, Beth, we swore we

wouldn't get that way till sixth grade. We even made it a rule, remember?"

"*You* watch it. You're telling our rules in front of an outsider."

"Aw, come on. Like it says in the song, 'Let's not fight,' okay?" Liz piled her blond hair up to the top of her head, held it there, closed her eyes, started singing sexily, " 'Let's not fight/ No, no, let's just be happy!' " It was a Glenda Tyrone song. "Come on, Beth, let's have Glenda for our idol, and Cameron can be our sub-idol, come on, what do you say?" Liz wheedled, smiled extra sweetly. "Please?"

Beth gave in. "All right."

"All *right!* Good, because I already sent away for Glenda posters, they'll look great in here. How many members d'you want to have?"

Last year it was just the two of them and Andrea Baylis. Andrea'd moved away.

Beth said, "How about four?"

Liz said, "Maybe. How about—" They went through about ten names, and couldn't decide.

Liz got impatient. "Why not just have three? That way it's more special. Now let's do secrets' insurance. Kneel, Janet. Here, in front of me. Close your eyes. Think of your favorite thing. Something extra special that you'd miss an awful lot if you didn't have it anymore. Okay, time's up. Tell what it is."

"Do I have to?"

"Yes."

"Okay. My jacks ball."

They looked like, What's special about that?

I described it. "It's like a crystal, only it's blue. It has stars inside. It's really beautiful."

"All right," said Liz, "now cross your heart and repeat after me: I, Janet Di Chocolate—"

"Di Ciocchio."

"Okay, I, Janet Whatever, do solemnly swear, by my jacks ball, that if I breathe a word to any living soul about this tree house, or about any club secret I may already have heard or am about to hear, then my jacks ball that's so special shall be forever forfeit."

"I, Janet, etc. Shall be forever what?"

"Forfeit. Gone," said Liz.

"Phht, just like that." Beth snapped her fingers. "Say it."

"Okay, 'shall be forever forfeit.' "

"Good. Uncross your heart. Arise," said Liz. "Go wait outside on the platform."

I did. They shut the door. While I was waiting I thought, Hey, I got through this whole thing without stuttering! And jinxed it. Should never even have thought it. The cottony feeling came into my mouth, and I knew I was going to.

They called me in. Liz asked, "Is there any special thing you can do that we can't?"

31

"And we don't mean jacks," Beth added scornfully.

I went, "P-p-p—"

Beth said, "She can stutter, but that doesn't count, does it, Liz?"

"Beth, cut it out. Let her answer."

"P-p-p—" Damn, I went through torture before I got it out, "P-p-play the piano."

Liz said, "Come show us."

We went back to the Fabers' front lawn. The party had moved inside. The piano was still out there.

"Sit down," Liz said. "Play 'Let's not fight.' "

"How does it go again?"

She sang it, and I picked out the tune.

"Now the theme from *How the Heart Yearns*." Beth hummed it.

I picked it out, no problem.

"She can play all right," said Liz.

Beth said, "Are we giving her a task?"

"Yes. *I* know, let's let her think up a name."

"For *our* club?"

"Yes. It always says 'creative' on her compositions. They get A's, and get put on the cork board. Let's see what she comes up with."

Beth sighed, like, okay, and gave in.

"Okay, Janet, your task is to think us up a good name for our club. One with dazzle. Will 32 you?"

"I'll try."

Then she asked me, "What's your favorite color?"

"Blue."

And she said, "Okay, let's all wear blue, the first day of school." Just like that. Like I was already in!

●●●●●●●●●●●

When I woke up next morning, I looked at myself in the mirror over my dresser. And I looked different. Well, I didn't have my glasses on. But it wasn't only that. I could already see myself thinner. I wasn't going to take one lick of ice cream, go anywhere near any fattening thing between then and when school started. And I already felt, well, almost pretty.

The sun shone in. My mirror gleamed. Old Bach and Beethoven on my wall—my piano teacher gave me those—seemed in better moods. Birds out my window chirped, just like every other morning, but that morning they sounded like a whole symphony orchestra and chorus to me.

I'd already started on my task. All the time I'd been sleeping, I was dreaming names. I knew that when I awoke I'd come up with one that would be just right. I looked out my window at our maple tree, as tall as the one the tree house **33** was in—and I had it, perfect! A name with a hint of the tree house in it, with my lucky number in it, and with a nice, mysterious sound to it, very secret. Plus, it even rhymed. They were going to love it!

I called up at the Fabers. I told it to Liz.

"It's good," she said. "I'll tell it to Beth. We'll call you later."

While I waited for them to call, I went through my closet and my dresser drawers. I tried on every item of blue clothing that I owned. Nothing looked that great. I definitely needed a new outfit.

I talked Mom into going to the mall. They have a Jordan Marsh there. I fell in love with a pair of jeans that the saleswoman said was "azure" blue, imported from France. And with a shirt that matched. I said, "Mom, aren't these fantastic?"

They cost a fortune. But I said I'd work it off by doing dishes, weeding in the garden, baby-sitting Joey, anything. And Mom bought them for me.

I wore them on Monday, with blue socks. Even my ponytail holder was blue. I got to school early and stood in the parking lot waiting for the Hyacinth Hills bus to pull in.

It came. Liz, Beth, and another girl got out. The three of them wore green from head to toe.

Aquamarine, or turquoise, whatever that green was called. A beautiful, light, bright green. But I decided I would hate that color till the day I died. Ditto, bits of mirror decorations. They had those on their shirts. The girl with Liz and Beth had reddish hair, green eyes, no glasses. She was thin and pretty, with silver dolphin earrings in her ears.

Luckily, just then the Soongs' car drove up. "Hi, Cory," I called as though I'd just been waiting for her, and we went inside together. Like nothing had happened.

During recess—indoors, because it had started to rain—Liz came over to me. She said, "Sorry, Janet. Thanks for the name. But you see, the thing is, this girl Vero moved into our neighborhood. And she does this really, really special thing. So we had to let her join. And—well, like it says in our new name, we can only be three, so, you understand, don't you? No hard feelings, okay?"

I clenched my fists inside my "azure" jeans pockets. Oh yes, oh yes, hard feelings!

Vero Jencks-Norris

April? Hey, can I call you Ape for short? When's your birthday? April first? No *fool*ing! Fun-*nee*. I had enough of that.

Vero, now there was a cool name. It went well with Jencks. The rest, the hyphen Norris part, wasn't *my* idea.

I used to live in a place like paradise. The Keys. They're little bits of islands, off the tip of Florida. The trees are always green there. One kind or another's always in bloom. And the sky is always full of birds, kinds you don't see other places. And the sea is shimmery green.

I was born in Sarasota. I've lived all over Florida, in St. Augustine, Tallahassee, Palm Beach, I don't remember all the places. Jencks—my father, but everybody called him that—didn't believe in staying put any one place too long. Fine with me, those were all cool places.

He used to be a golf pro. When I was about four years old, my mom split. Around that time, Jencks switched to tennis. We moved down to the Keys and he landed jobs as tennis pro at all the nice resorts there. The coolest one was Caiman's Creek on Key Islamorada. It had two clay courts, six all-weather courts, a sweet-water pool, a saltwater pool, three hundred feet of sandy beach, a marina. And they gave us our own bungalow with a hammock strung between two palm trees.

I changed schools so many times, I got used to it. It was a snap. School work came easy to me. So did the social part. I always had plenty of kids to hang out with, have fun with, but not get too attached. Why bother, when, in a couple of months, we'd be moving to the next place?

And anyway, I liked to spend time on my own, down at the beach, or at the backboard, working on my strokes, or watching Jencks give lessons. The best times were when he wasn't busy and would hit with me. You never saw anyone zing balls over the net the way he did, at a hundred miles an hour! If I returned one of those, he'd say, "Keep 'em coming like that, and *you'll* be the pro!"

But he got tired of tennis. He said, "Life's too short to keep doing the same old thing over and over." He took up boats, hung around the marina, signed on as crew on fishing and excursion trips. When the resort guests complained that they couldn't get lessons, the place hired a new pro, a grouchy guy who didn't want me hanging around the courts.

That was okay with me. I didn't mind, because Jencks took me along on the boat trips. They were great. For the first half hour, anyway. Then I'd get queasy. Things would start reeling, I'd feel like I was on a combination see-saw and merry-go-round. And I'd be sick as a dog.

"Don't look down at the water," Jencks would say. "Here, suck on this," and he'd give me sour candy. "You'll be fine." But I wasn't.

Nothing helped. When you're that seasick, you wish the boat would capsize so you could drown and get it over with. You throw up all the time. You don't care where you do it. One time I did it all over the white sandals of this lady, Mrs. Sherrington. Not on purpose, although she might have thought so. I didn't like her a whole lot. And she didn't like me, either.

"Sherry," Jencks called her. He went down on his knees, cleaned her toes. And apologized for me.

She had a figure like Madonna. She had platinum hair, a great big rock of a diamond ring, and eyelashes out to there.

I was standing at the bow, leaning over the railing, in case I had to throw up more, when I noticed the name painted onto the boat. *Sherry.* It was hers. I'd thought it belonged to Caiman's.

Jencks gave me a pep talk. "Just make up your mind you can lick this seasick thing. I'm counting on you."

38　　　Okay, I made up my mind. I went along every

chance I got. I'd start out fine. Then in half an hour, my stomach would heave, same old thing.

One day last spring we were cruising around in Florida Bay—Jencks and Sherry, this honeymoon couple, Dan and Lee Ann Tobias, and me. The weather was perfect. We'd been going for almost two hours, and, hey, I still felt okay! Jencks was proud of me. He said, " 'Atta girl, I knew you'd lick it."

That part of the Bay has thousands of hummocks. Those are clumps of mangrove trees that rooted themselves in the water. They had all these birds on them—blue herons, pink spoonbills, white ibises, and egrets, and pelicans. The sky was cloudless, and there was a nice, fresh breeze. "Perfect," Dan Tobias said. "This has to be what the Garden of Eden looked like, the day before God got around to creating people."

Sherry wiggled out of her sundress. "Anyone feel like a dip?" And, *whoosh,* she was in.

Jencks dropped anchor. He was only wearing his cutoffs, so he didn't have to take off anything. He jackknifed in, perfect, almost no splash, and snuck up on Sherry, grabbed her, ducked her under. They stayed down pretty long.

When she came up she made a big thing of swimming away from him to the other side of the boat.

39

"Hon, come on in," Jencks called to me and surface-dived under, chasing after Sherry.

Swimming was my favorite thing. I'd learned really young. I felt as at home in the water as on land. I'd jump and dive off any place, the higher the better.

I took off the shorts and shirt that I was wearing over my swimsuit, dived in, and everything went black. I'd hit my head on something—the side of the boat, a rock, I don't know what. For a second I didn't feel anything. Then it hurt. A lot. Like the pain was going to swallow me up, or rather, down. Florida Bay is only about twelve feet deep, but I felt like I was sinking a hundred feet.

Little bubbles floated around me. Bubbles from my breath. I wondered, in a weird, calm way, like it had no importance and nobody'd care, least of all me, if those bubbles were the air from the last breath I'd ever take.

Next thing I remember, Dan Tobias was giving me mouth-to-mouth resuscitation.

"Jencks?" First I didn't see him.

"Here I am, hon." He took his arm from around Sherry's waist and came over to help me sit up. "Feeling better?"

My head hurt. Not that much. But I was parched. From swallowing seawater, I guess. And nauseous. Seasick as a dog. Even with the boat perfectly still. I hadn't "licked" this thing at all, like Jencks had counted on me to. I felt like a real flop.

Lee Ann brought me water. It tasted good. "Thanks." I waited for Jencks to say something.

He went "Phew. You're okay now, aren't you?" Then he said, "Sorry, honey," to Sherry, put his arm around her. "I didn't want anything to spoil this day."

A shiny silver arc flashed out of the water just then, right nearby. Sherry went, "Oo, look, a flying shark!"

It was dolphins. Two of them. I stood up to watch. I felt a little dizzy. And everybody told me to go lie down.

I had a better view from below. The dolphins swam right up to the porthole. First one, then the other. Then a baby one. I saw them from really close. They had funny-shaped noses. Their wide mouths curved up like they were smiling. Their green eyes looked as though they were thinking, the same way people do.

By then I was woozy, drifting in and out of sleep. The dolphins kept swimming around the boat and back to the porthole, like they wanted to tell me something. Whenever I opened my eyes, there'd be one of them, looking at me close up, almost tapping its nose against the porthole. Like it was saying, Pay attention! Like, it was promising that if I could just concentrate on it and the other dolphins, then the other stuff, the nearly drowning, would go away, like those parts of the day never happened.

č

After that, Jencks seemed kind of nervous around me. He kept saying that we needed to have a good, long talk. But then he didn't get around to it. I hoped it wouldn't be about Sherry. The only good news on that subject would have been that he was through with her. And I knew darn well he wasn't.

One night in June we were down at the marina looking at the boats, watching the stars come out. And he said, "Hon, I'm going fishing for a couple of days. Nancy Lynn'll stay with you." She ran the dining room at Caiman's. I liked her okay.

I said, "Have a great time."

"Thanks. *You* have a great time." Like I was the one going someplace.

Then we went to Papa Billy's Diner that Jencks said had the best Key Lime pie of anyplace in the Keys, and we had some. "How about another, for farewell?" Jencks said.

"But you'll only be gone a couple of days."

"Right. A so-long slice. How about it?"

The next day was the last day of school. We all came out whooping and yelling. Then I saw this strange woman standing there. She was really young. She had a pretty dress on, the color of cinnamon, same color as her short, zippy hair.

Something about her made me get all shy. That was weird, because I was used to all different kinds of people; I was never shy! I looked away, stared at the ground. And that was weird too, because all I really wanted to do was look at her face, keep looking at it, eat it up with my eyes.

She held her arms out. She said "April?" So then I knew.

After she'd split, I asked Jencks where she'd gone, and he said, "To find herself." How come? I couldn't see how a person got lost from herself in the first place. Then when I got older, I figured it probably had to do with me getting born when she was only sixteen and a half, still almost a kid herself. That was probably rough on her.

She was even shier than me. Blowing her nose. Saying those corny things, "You've grown. I'd have known you anywhere."

She went home to the bungalow with me.

No sign of Nancy Lynn. Of course not. Because Jencks had known all along. There was a note on my bed: "Hon, I've been the lucky one, having you with me all this time. Now it's your mom's turn for awhile. I know you'll have a great summer. I got you a going-away present. But it isn't ready yet. So I'll send it. Love ya. Jencks."

Mom and I fixed dinner. I showed her where we kept the pots and pans, glasses, knives, forks. I was making believe she'd come to stay with us for good, and that when Jencks got back we'd be a happy family. I was having the kind of time that little kids have playing house.

Then when we were eating, she asked, "How would you like to be a bridesmaid?" And I thought, Hey, it's coming true!

But next morning we drove to Miami in her rented car and got on a plane to Boston.

I still felt very shy with her. Ditto, she with me. Especially after I blurted, "Mom, when you—um—went away, did you find yourself?"

She laughed. She said, "Well, I sure looked all over. Even back at my parents' in Sacramento, California. They let me move back in." She went "Whew," like she was glad that was over. "I finished high school, went to Boston, to college. And then, I'll tell you what I *did* find"—a big happy smile came on her face—"the greatest guy, Norri. He's the best thing that ever happened to me. No, I take it back." She took both my hands. "The best thing is getting my beautiful daughter back."

I didn't know where to look, I was so embarrassed.

44   Edward Everett Norris—Norri—was waiting

at the gate when the plane landed. Boy, what a letdown. I'd figured that to be better looking than Jencks, which was hard to imagine, this "greatest guy ever" would have to look like Tom Cruise, or Bruce Willis, somebody like that.

He had hardly any hair, and he was really skinny. He and Mom kissed about a hundred times. Then he shook hands with me. I was wondering what I was supposed to call him. He said, "You can call me Norri too, if that's okay with you."

Okay. I had a fake smile all prepared in case he gave me the rigmarole of, You and I are going to be good friends. But he skipped that.

He drove us to his mother's house. We all stayed there till the wedding.

Mom bought me a peach-colored dress, peach-colored shoes, and a wreath kind of thing for my hair. And a bunch of other stuff: shorts, shirts, underwear, socks, bathing suits, a flashlight. I was going to this camp, Mohantic, in New Hampshire, where Norri'd gone summers when he was a kid. He and Mom had it all arranged, and it was okay with Jencks.

The wedding was at the Ritz Hotel in a ball-room with mirrors and chandeliers and flowers all over the place.

I was the maid of honor. I did the ring part

okay. But in the part where the minister asked, "Do you, Edward Everett, take this woman, Margaret etcetera, and do you, Margaret, take this man," I squeezed my eyes half-closed, squinted Norri out of the picture, put Jencks in. If that was not what the maid of honor should have been doing, so what, nobody knew.

They went to Europe on their honeymoon. I stayed at Norri's mother's for the two weeks between then and when camp would start.

Norri's mom was thin as a string bean, same as Norri, with gray hair parted in the middle, pinned up in the back, and she wore serious-looking clothes, suits and dresses, all the time.

She showed me the tourist sights—Bunker Hill, the Old South Church, and where the Boston Tea Party happened. One time she showed me a courthouse, took me inside. I asked, "What historical thing happened here?" Nothing. It turned out she was on vacation now, but when she worked, she worked right in that courthouse. She was a judge. People called her "Your Honor."

Cool. I tried calling her that. She raised an eyebrow, was I being disrespectful? No, I just liked how it sounded.

One time she asked, "Do you have grandparents?"

46   "Well, yes, and no. Jencks's parents died before I was born. And Mom's parents live out west, I never met them."

"I see," she said in a clipped voice, like she thought that was too bad. "Well, I have no grandchildren."

I hoped she wasn't leading up to making me call her Grandma. No. Good. All she meant was, we were kind of in the same boat.

We got along okay. I had a pretty good time with her. Days, anyway.

Nights, I missed Jencks like crazy. And I couldn't even talk to him on the phone. He'd quit Caiman's Creek and was cruising around the Caribbean. On the *Sherry,* I kind of figured. One time he called me, from the Bahamas. He said he was figuring out what he wanted to do next. It was a bad connection. I said, "Will you have it figured out by fall?" Static, static. But I heard him say, "You bet." And that my present was on its way.

On July first it still hadn't come.

Then Norri's mother drove me up to Camp Mohantic.

I liked it right away. The weather was clear and breezy. There were mountains all around. And there was a big lake that looked great. I'd never swum in a lake before. I couldn't wait to get in it. My two weeks in Boston were the longest I'd ever gone without swimming.

47

The director said, "This package came for you," and handed it to me. It was my present from Jencks—silver dolphin earrings.

I put them in my ears.

Norri's mother said, "They're lovely, April."

I thought how the kids I was about to meet would ask, could they call me Ape, etc. Then I noticed that the package was postmarked Vero Beach. That caught my eye. Vero, nice, I liked that. And nobody knew me here, so why not? I'd just tell everyone that was my name.

Norri's mother and the camp director were busy talking over old times. They didn't notice the little ceremony I went through:

First I touched my fingertips to the dolphins in my ears. Then to my heart. Then to my lips. I whispered, under my breath, "I hereby rename myself Vero," and I bet it would be a great summer.

They had the lake roped off into sections: Shallow, for the little kids who didn't know how to swim yet. Medium-deep, for intermediates. The deep part was the biggest, with three floats. It looked so inviting!

The first time my division, the Beavers, were scheduled for swim, I rushed in ahead of the other kids, ducked under the ropes, headed for **48** the floats.

"Come back here," the waterfront counselor yelled.

You were supposed to take a test first: dive in, swim to a marker about twenty feet away and back—real easy.

"Something wrong?" called the guy. Because I was standing at the edge of the diving board like my feet were screwed to it.

"No—" Yes, there was. I didn't know what to call it. Fear? That didn't tell the half of it. I'd never felt anything like it. "Do I have to go in head first?"

"You're supposed to. But okay, jump in, if you'd rather."

"Thanks." I held my nose, took a little hop first, the way I always did. But then the water looked so far below, and the same thing happened. I froze.

"Go," said kids behind me.

"Go on," said the waterfront guy.

I couldn't. I was terrified. I said, "I don't feel so well. I'll come back later."

I came back later that day, and the next day, and the next. But it kept happening. The counselor, Mark, was a good guy. He said I could go off the dock instead of the diving board, and he jumped in himself. "See, nothing to it."

"I know." But I was just too scared. Scared to

death to dive or jump in. Not of swimming, though. I was dying to, I wanted to swim so badly I could taste it.

"Couldn't I just walk in? Please? I'm a good swimmer, honest."

"Only in the shallow section. Sorry, those are the rules." He offered to work with me more. He was sure I could get over being scared. But I couldn't.

And rather than go in the shallow section with the "Tadpoles," non-swimmers, I didn't go in at all. I told the other Beavers that I had an ear infection. And they bought it.

Beavers? A chicken was what I'd turned into. I was so ashamed!

One night I put on pajamas over my bathing suit. Then, after everyone was asleep, I took a towel, my flashlight, and I sneaked down to the lake. I thought maybe with no one around to watch I could lick this thing.

I went out on the diving board, stood there, head down, arms forward. I thought, Nothing to it, I've done it hundreds of times. But I was too scared. And also, I got this really sharp pain in the back of my head.

I tried to jump off the dock. But I was just as scared to. I just couldn't. I thought, What if this whole dock was on fire? Well, I still couldn't have. I'd have burned to ashes.

I walked into the water, swam out past the ropes into the deep part, swam around there, like I'd been wanting to. But it was cold, and my head still hurt. I didn't stay in long.

I stole back into my bunk. And I stayed away from the waterfront the whole rest of the time.

Without swimming, camp was a drag. I couldn't wait for it to end. Jencks wrote me that he was thinking of starting a sailing school, how would I like that? He wasn't sure where yet, but he'd know by Labor Day. Cool. I counted the days.

ی

On the last day of camp, Mom and Norri came for me with a trunkload of presents from Europe—costumed dolls, a cuckoo clock, a statue of the Eiffel Tower, stuff like that.

"Thanks!" I tried to sound enthusiastic. Where would I keep it all? No place of Jencks's would have room for so much stuff.

Norri's car was elegant, with real leather upholstery. I had the whole backseat to stretch out in. But I couldn't get comfortable—with them, I mean.

Or they with me. They had something on their minds, I could feel it all the time that they were telling me about places they'd been, things they'd seen on their trip.

Then Mom asked, "How come kids called you Vera?"

"Ver*o*," I said. "It's a nickname."

"Camp's the place to get those," Norri said. "I got called some that you wouldn't believe."

Mom said, "I like April better. April, listen, I—we—Now don't get upset, okay? Norri and I want you to live with us."

"You mean, till Jencks finds a place?"

Mom stared straight ahead, I could see in the mirror. And she didn't answer.

"For how long, Mom?"

Norri took a hand off the wheel, put it over hers. "Want me to tell her?"

"No, I will." Mom turned around to me. She gripped the top of her seat. "Norri and I've talked about this a lot. Jencks—well, he's—oh, you know." Her voice got clenched talking about him. "Norri would like to adopt you. So legally he'd be your father—"

Far out! I had to laugh.

Mom looked like that was very rude. "How is that funny?"

"Sorry." I was picturing Jencks, how he'd throw his head back and laugh really loud. I said, "I was just thinking what Jencks would say."

Mom grasped Norri's arm, like, she couldn't say this part.

"Jencks of course will always be your real father," Norri said. "But—" He could see my face in the rearview mirror. "Are you feeling okay? You look a little greenish under that good tan."

I said, "I feel okay."

So then he told me, "Jencks agreed. He thought it was a good idea."

I didn't believe it.

The air-conditioning was on full blast. But it felt hot in the car. I felt like I couldn't breathe. Where was the knob to roll my window down? There wasn't one. Instead there was an electronic gizmo that you touched, and the window went down by itself. I did that. I felt so sick, sure I was going to throw up. But I didn't. I just had the dry heaves.

Norri pulled into the breakdown lane and stopped the car. Mom said, "Get in the front. That helps when you're carsick." And she changed seats with me.

The next stop was Gifford, Massachusetts.

They'd bought a house in a ritzy neighborhood there. On seven acres of land. Norri was a lawyer for big banks and businesses, he earned lots of money, he could afford all that.

My room was bigger than our whole bungalow at Caiman's. It had pretty curtains, a flouncy bedspread, a dressing table with a skirt. Mom had gone to a lot of trouble decorating it. And she'd filled up the closet and bureau with expensive-looking clothes that all fit me okay. But when I looked in the mirror I looked like a stranger to myself.

One thing I liked was that the seven acres of land was almost all woods. Walking around in the woods was about the only thing I felt like doing. My life had gotten turned inside out and upside down, and I was miserable. At least in the woods I didn't need to worry about trying not to show it.

Then I found something that gave me a lift— a tree house. I thought Mom and Norri were planning to surprise me with it. It was cool, just what I needed. A place to be private, think my own thoughts. Or, *not* think, even better.

I spent a lot of time just looking out the windows. I saw where squirrels kept their acorn stashes. I listened to woodpeckers drilling in a tree for bugs. Once I saw a deer and watched it for as long as it hung around. I imagined being those animals. They had it simple. They stayed in their nests or wherever they lived, with whichever parent took care of them, maybe both, and no getting shunted back and forth.

But then one time I started up the ladder steps, and someone yelled, "No trespassing!"

I went on up anyway.

Two girls came out on the platform, one blond, one with brown hair. "Who're you?"

"This is *my* tree house," said the blond. "And it's private."

"Oh. I thought it was on our property." I said who I was and that we'd just moved here. My face ached from smiling at them so hard, to make them like me, so they'd let me in.

They did. And I saw that they'd been doing things to the place. Painting the inside of the door pink. Putting posters up.

"Sorry, I didn't know I was trespassing. I just love this place, etc." I talked a blue streak, scared that once I stopped they'd make me leave.

They gave me the once-over. The one with brown hair stared at my chest. I thought she was checking if my bosoms were growing faster than hers. No, she was pointing at Caiman's Creek Resort. I was wearing my shirt with a picture of it and two alligators on it. "Have you been to that place?"

"Yeah."

She knew about it. She said, "My parents rated it tops, five stars."

"It's nice. I've been to other great places." I told them a few.

They were impressed. They asked what school I'd be going to, what grade.

Ludcomb Middle School, fifth grade, same as them.

"Hey, Liz, I have a great idea," said the brown-haired girl, Beth. They went in a corner and whispered.

Then they sat me down and asked me more questions. What was my zodiac sign, birthstone, favorite singer, etc. And, "Can you do anything that's really special?"

I mentioned a bunch of things—caddy, spot hard-to-see golf balls, tee off, play tennis. But either they didn't count, or Liz and Beth could do them too, and it had to be something they couldn't.

I had to think of something great, so they'd let me keep coming here. What, though?

While I was wracking my brains, the blond one, Liz, said, "Can I see your earrings? Are those dolphins?"

I thought, Thank you, dolphins. It was like they were helping me out. I touched them with my fingertips. I thought, Help me out more! And this place came into my mind that I'd seen ads for down in the Keys, a place where they let you swim with dolphins. A woman Jencks was seeing before Sherry used to talk about it. She'd done it. She said the dolphins swam up really close, and wanted you to touch them, and made all kinds of clucks and chirping noises that if you could only understand were probably whole long stories about their lives in the sea.

56 "I really like your earrings," Liz said.

"Thank you." And thanks a whole lot, dolphins, for giving me the idea. I said, "Yes, I can do something special. Swim with dolphins."

"You did that? Weren't you scared? Hey, that is special. All right, now you have to do a task," said Liz.

"*I* know, let's let her do our nails," said Beth. She took bottles of nail polish out of her backpack, one pink, one a weird color, green.

They gave me instructions: First a coat of pink. Then, with green polish, draw the letter T on their thumb, middle-finger, and pinkie nails. Then, green number three's on their other two nails. It was some kind of code for the name of their club.

I hated the smell of nail polish. And it was a tricky job. But I did it extra carefully without any goofs.

When I was done, they made me swear not to tell anyone if they told me the name. Okay, I swore. Then they painted my nails the same way, and told me the name, and asked me to join.

I said, "Sure!" I didn't care what they did in their club. Their club could have been for digging worms, frying them up with grits, eating them for breakfast, anything. I'd still have joined, just to be allowed to keep on coming to the tree house. And they said I could, anytime I wanted.

$\mathcal{L}$aura Hoffman

The weather turned warm. People talked about how it was the warmest February in years. The pond unfroze. Only the Supes stayed icy to me. Like I'd never guessed their password. Like they'd never asked me all those questions, or said anything about giving me a task, or come to my house.

One thing I was glad about: Janet didn't act mad that I hadn't called her. She didn't even say anything about it.

Good. I invited her over.

She came on Thursday. It was sixty degrees out. We sat on our deck. The air smelled of spring.

I went down to the edge of the pond, dipped my hand in. Not too cold. I asked, "Do people swim in this pond?"

Janet said, "No. It gets pretty weedy. And it has snapping turtles. It's good for fishing, though. Hey, what's that noise?"

Max came crashing through some bushes.

Labradors can move really fast. They can look scary to people not used to dogs. Especially when they've been running and are panting and their tongues hang out. He came bounding up the steps.

Janet flattened herself against the wall of the house.

I grabbed him. "Take it easy, Max." I let him lick my face, and I held on to his collar so he wouldn't go sniff at Janet. That was just how he got acquainted with people, but she wouldn't have liked it. I said, "Janet, don't be scared, he's really gentle."

So then she came over, not too close, and touched him, with the tip of one finger. "Hi, Max."

"Maxie, do your trick, come on." The only trick he knew. I held my hand out. "Shake."

He thought it over, decided, Oh all right, put it there. And got that sweet, give-me-compliments look on his face.

"Good dog, good dog." I scratched between his ears. "Now shake with Janet."

She bravely put her hand out. Max could always smell it when people were scared of him, and that hurt his feelings. So I thought he might not do it. But he did it, gave her his paw.

"He likes me!" Janet got over being so afraid and started petting him.

"Good boy, Max. Good for you, Janet." The way she was making friends with him made me **62** think of Vero not even wanting to see him. I must have frowned or something, because Janet asked, "What's wrong?"

"Oh, just, well, the day I didn't call you? The Supes came over." I told her the whole thing.

She stared down at the deck planks the whole time. She was pretty hurt that I'd gone skating, but not with her. She said, "And now they act like they don't even know you. Typical. 'Cause now they don't need a place to change. That's just how they are." She shrugged. "I've been through it. I know all about it. Let's not talk about it anymore, okay?"

A week went by. The weather stayed warm, and the Supes stayed frozen. To me, anyway. Especially Vero.

And the thing that made it even worse was, Mary Lou kept asking, "What's happening with those girls? Are they letting you join their club?"

I felt like a fool. I wished I hadn't told her.

Then, one night—I was already in bed, I'd just about given up the whole thing—Mom called me to the phone. And it was Beth.

"Hi, Laura, how's it going?" She sounded really friendly. "I hope it's not too late to call. Me and Liz were just talking, and we were wondering if—Can I ask you something?"

"Sure, go ahead."

"It's about Janet. You're friends with her, so we thought maybe you could help us out. You **63** know that name she calls us, 'Supes?' It hurts our feelings. You can understand that, can't you? Wouldn't it hurt your feelings too, if somebody called you that?"

"Yeah, I guess so."

"Well, could you try and talk to her about it? Get her to quit? That would be so nice of you."

"I could try."

"Say you will. Come on, Laura." She made it sound really important.

"Okay, I'll try."

"Good, try extra hard." All the Supe-iness came back into her voice. "Give it your best shot, Laura. Because it's your task!" And she hung up.

—————

The next day I was over at Janet's. She gave me a jacks demonstration. She did really hard things that I'd never even heard of—Dog Paddle, Goats on the Mountain. The way her fingers swooped around doing acrobatics made it look like a whole other thing, not such a baby game.

She tried to sharpen me up, give me pointers, so I'd get better at it, and join the game she and her friends had going.

Her brother Joey kept barging in. He's cute but a pain. He kept going for the ball. One time he grabbed it away just when I'd gotten a good throw. Janet tried to pry his fingers loose. But he scooted away and monster-jumped and danced around the room, laughing, going, "Nyah, nyah," and wouldn't give it back.

"I give up," Janet said, and called out the window, "Dad, help! Come get Joey!"

Mr. Di Ciocchio came up and was nice about it. He said, "Joey, come on down with me, I need you in the yard, I'm clearing brush." He made it sound like he couldn't do a good job without Joey helping. Meantime he'd quietly gotten the ball away from him and slipped it to Janet. "So long, girls, see you later."

So then we had peace. Janet did Flipsies. Those were impossible. She made me try, and I did lousy. I said, "This is too hard! I can't do it."

"Sure you can, watch." She caught five jacks on the backs of her hands, like, nothing to it.

"You make it look so easy!" And I got an idea. "Hey, Janet? Did you ever think that could be your special thing?"

"You mean, for getting into the Supes?"

"Mm hm."

She scowled. "What makes you think I'd want to?"

"Well, you said, you'd been through it, so—"

"So nothing. So they'd just laugh. They look down on jacks. And anyway, I do a more special thing."

"Like what?"

"Play the piano. Like you'd expect, with my mom and my dad both being pianists."

So I asked, "Would you play something for me?"

"Okay."

We went downstairs. They have this whole music room in their basement. Janet played three pieces.

I applauded. She was good. I asked, "Do the Su—, I mean, do Liz, Beth, and Vero know you can play?"

"Yeah. I played for them. Liz and Beth, anyway. Vero wasn't there yet."

"So what happened?"

"N-n-nothing. It didn't work out, that's all."

"Listen, Janet, it still could." I'd gotten this whole other idea. "Want to know what you should do?"

"What?"

"Stop calling them 'Supes.' "

"Why? I like to. It's fun."

"It sounds mean, though. It hurts their feelings."

"*They're* mean. *They* hurt people's feelings, all the time!" Janet did her scowl at me, and looked suspicious. "How come you care so much about their feelings, all of a sudden? Let me think." She tapped her forehead, like to make her brain work faster. "*I* know. They gave you a task, didn't they? And it's getting me not to call them 'Supes.' So that's what you're doing, right?" Her eyes went darker, almost black. And she looked into mine. It was a staring contest.

I lost, I looked away first.

"You see? I'm right." She shot up from the piano bench, slammed the lid down. "And you know what, Laura? I'll call them 'Supes' even more, I'll never stop. And you know what else? You don't care if I do anything special or not. You were just trying to use me, to get yourself into the Supes. Well, good luck!"

I felt like two cents. "Janet, listen—"

"No, *you* listen. You're wasting your time. You could do a million tasks for them, and they still wouldn't let you in. They can't. Except if one of them dropped dead or something."

"How come?"

"Because their club is just for three."

"How do you know?"

"Because it says so in their name. *I* made it up. Because that was *my* task. You don't believe me, do you? You think they'd never have asked a nobody like me to do a thing like that for them, right?" Her face was on fire from being so mad. "I'll tell it to you. The name of their club is 'The Tree-Top Three.'"

"Why 'Tree-Top'?"

"None of your business. Now do you believe me?"

"Yes."

"Good." But she sounded like nothing would ever be good again. She took her jacks ball out of her pocket. She bounced it, hard. It went straight up to the ceiling. Then it bounced all over the room and she didn't catch it, like she didn't want it anymore. Finally it rolled under the piano.

I got down to get it.

She shook her head, "No, don't."

So I let it lie.

She was leaning against the shelves of books and music, looking at me in this funny way. Like she hated being so mad at me. Like she was waiting for me to say something to make things better.

I wanted to, but I didn't know what.

Then it was too late. She was at the door. "Ah—um—" She glared at me, like everything was my fault, including that her stutter was back, really bad now. "I'm g-g-going to c-c-clear brush." She marched upstairs.

And I went home.

———————

On the weekend our family went into Boston. **68** We'd planned to go just on Saturday. But there was so much to see, we went again Sunday. We had a great time, and it took my mind off the mess I was in with Janet.

But then Monday morning, when I got near our classroom, I heard the *kick-kick-kick* sound. That was strange. Because the Supes had quit doing that. Besides, it was only twenty of nine, and their bus never came till ten of.

Well, when I went in, there were Janet, Cory, Shawna, and Julie, sitting on the windowsill, kicking away, wearing cardboard badges that said "NOBS!"

When they saw me, they kicked harder. And they looked away.

Great. A whole other club I wasn't in.

At nine of nine the Supes arrived. They were mad as hornets. They went into a huddle, held a council of war. The windowsill went the length of the room, there was plenty of space. But they didn't get up there too. What, and share their territory? They were too proud for that. All they did, at least for now, was stick their noses in the air and pretend nothing had happened.

Tuesday they came early. The Hendersons' housekeeper drove them. They got there at twenty-one minutes of nine, one minute before Mr. Kaplow, the custodian, opened the door. The Nobs were there too. The two clubs crowded in.

69

They rushed up the stairs, dashed down the hall, and raced like crazy to the windowsill.

Cory, the shortest and skinniest, was really fast. Beth was no slouch either. Those two were neck and neck.

Cory won by a split second, and claimed the sill for the Nobs.

"S-S-Supes, stand back!" yelled Janet.

"Yeah, stand back, Supes," yelled all the Nobs.

The Supes grabbed the Nobs by the ankles, legs, sweaters, arms, and yanked and pulled.

In the middle of this battle Ms. Tatum came in. "What is this, kindergarten? Cut it out!" she bellowed, like through a bullhorn.

They froze.

"Take off those ridiculous badges. Julie and Shawna, go to your own classroom. The rest of you, take your seats. You have thirty seconds.

"All right, now listen. I'll say this only once: The windowsill is off limits, except to Gus and Gil"—the guinea pigs' cage was up there—"And no club stuff, do you hear me? No badges. Not in *my* classroom. Is that clear?"

"Yes, Ms. Tatum."

"Okay. That is that, I trust."

70   But it was not. It just got the clubs going more.

How come teachers, even ones like Ms. Tatum, who could be pretty understanding, didn't understand that? When clubs got forbidden, it only made kids want to join them more.

Going down the stairs to recess, the Nobs whisked out their badges, stuck them back on.

As soon as they hit the playground, they raced the Supes to the climbing bars. Cory'd gotten all this confidence from winning the windowsill race. She won again and started climbing.

They grabbed her legs. They yanked. She lost her grip and fell. She scraped her knees. Her tights were ripped, but her knees weren't bloody. So Mrs. Hollis, the teacher on playground duty, didn't make her go to the nurse.

Next day, her knees must still have hurt. She didn't run as fast. The Supes won the windowsill. The idea was to get down way before Ms. Tatum arrived. But they were so thrilled with themselves, they stayed up there too long and got caught.

"I warned you," said Ms. Tatum, and started writing them passes to go to the office.

Liz turned pale.

"Please, Ms. Tatum, give us one more chance?" Beth begged.

"All right, just this once." Ms. Tatum made them get Wall-Wipe and sponges from Mr. Kap- **71** low's supply closet, and they had to scrub all the kick marks off the wall. Of course, a lot of those had been made by the Nobs. So the Supes thought that was unfair and couldn't wait to get revenge.

One day the next week we had a substitute, Mrs. Keithley, who was known for being easy, never sent kids to the office.

The Supes passed notes around, "NOBS ARE SLOBS!"

So then the Nobs passed notes, "SUPES ARE GOOPS!" They even wrote it on the board in giant letters.

When Ms. Tatum came back, it went on like that, only in secret. Which, as I said, only made it more exciting. And rougher on kids on the outside. Like me.

Wednesday night after dinner, Mom and Dad were watching the news on TV downstairs. I went up to their bedroom because *Dolphin Cove* was on, and I wanted to watch that.

The dolphins were in danger. The marine-mammal research team had set these clever traps for them. The chief researcher's daughter, Rose Ellen, tried to warn the dolphins to stay away. Something like that. I lost track of the plot. I just liked watching her swim with them.

Mary Lou came in and watched for a minute.

She'd passed her pre-audition for Thespians, so now she was a big judge of acting. "The humans in that show are really bad," she said. "But I don't see anything sad happening, so how come you're crying?"

"You see those rocks on that beach? See that space in between? I feel like I fell into someplace like that. Because now there are *two* clubs that don't want me." I clicked off the TV and told her my whole situation. "What do you think I should do?"

"Well, if it was me, before I knocked myself out trying to get into any club, I'd make sure that club *did* something interesting. Like, put on plays or something."

"Like Thespians, but that's high school. Come on, pretend you're back in fifth grade for a sec."

"In fifth grade I was in 'Mugwumps,' and we had a bake sale for the summer camp scholarship fund."

"Good for you. You were real humanitarians. Look, Mary Lou, I don't need a sermon." I clicked *Dolphin Cove* back on. Mary Lou said, "Here's what I think. You should make up with Janet. It sounds to me like she's just waiting for you to."

"I tried."

"Try some more."

So I did. But all that happened every time was, it brought on Janet's stutter, and she'd walk away, like she'd gotten allergic to me.

So then, to give her a break from me, I moved to a table in the back of the room with kids who at least didn't hate me. And I hung around a lot by myself.

One afternoon Mom picked me up from school by surprise. She was in a great mood. She'd read in her college alumnae magazine that her freshman roommate, Maureen Parslow, who she'd lost touch with, lived in Halsey, the next town, only five miles away.

"I called her up," Mom said. "She couldn't believe it, it's been twenty years! She said to come right over. She can't wait to meet you. She's got two boys, one your age."

The one my age was Steve. He had dark hair, huge feet, a mouth full of braces, and he acted like he thought girls were an alien species.

He showed me the stuff in their family room. His mother had told him to. Their fish tank, his drums, his brother's swimming trophies. And a Nintendo he was itching to get at.

He had a new game for it, "The Adventures of DinoRiki." It was about a boy and prehistoric animals from a billion B.C. on up through time. **74** The object was for the boy to conquer them with different weapons and to evolve into Macho-Riki.

Steve was really into it. I thought it was gross. I was about ready to go hang around Mom and Mrs. Parslow. But then Steve's brother walked in.

He was sixteen, maybe seventeen. He wore a letter sweater and was truly handsome. I could imagine if I were older, wow. I'd rate him at least nine and a half on Mary Lou's and Stacey's chart. Too bad Mary Lou was at Stacey's, rehearsing for the Thespians audition. She was going to be very sorry that she missed out on meeting him.

"Hi, I'm Mark. Good to meet you, Laura. Mom says you live in Gifford. I knew somebody from there, your age."

"You did? What was her name?"

And he said, "Vero."

"No kidding? Vero Jencks-Norris, she's in my class! Where did you meet her?"

"At this camp I worked at. How's she doing?"

"Fine. Steve showed me your swimming trophies. Were you the swimming counselor?"

"Yes, I was."

"Vero must have won lots of trophies, too."

"Not nice." He laughed, as though I'd made a nasty joke.

"What do you mean? She's a great swimmer." **75**

He asked, "Did you ever see her swim?"

"No, but I know she's good. She'd have to be. She swam with dolphins in Florida."

"Really? That's strange. She only went in the water one time. She couldn't pass the simple swimming test that every camper had to take," said Mark.

Janet Di Ciocchio

• • • • • • • • • •

Seeing Cory on the windowsill gave me the idea. It was her week for taking care of the guinea pigs. She was changing the wood shavings in their cage. Mr. Kaplow had pushed it right up against the window like he always did when he dusted. And Cory was so short, the only way she could reach into it was to get up there herself.

My idea was perfect, simple. It felt so right! I got up there with her. "Hey, Cory, why don't *we* start a club?"

"Yeah! Why don't we?"

We went and got Julie and Shawna.

Cory said, "Us four, and Laura, right?"

I said, "Just us four. Not Laura."

"How come? I thought she was your friend."

"I thought so too. But she'd rather be a Supe." I told them about her task and all.

Okay, not Laura, they agreed. And we agreed that not just me, but all of us, would call them 'Supes,' all the time, because they had it coming.

At recess we decided that the playground steps would be our club territory. We held a meeting and decided what our club would be for: fun and friendship. And what against: the Supes. We'd be enemies of everything they stood for.

Just as we were talking about them, who should do us the honor of coming over to bother us but Liz and Beth, and we had to adjourn.

We met at my house after school. Joey was at his friend Chuck's house, so we had peace and quiet, and decided more things:

1) Not to act superior.

2) Not to be snobs.

3) Not to go out of our way to make non-members feel bad.

Then Shawna said, "But what if we can't help it and start doing those things, just because now we're a club?"

"We won't," said Julie. "We'll never be like that. We'll stay our same old selves, that's all."

"Right, same old nobodies," I said.

Cory said, "Nobodies, I like that. How about that for our name?"

We all liked it. "Nobs" for short. And our password could be "Nobodies Forever."

"Let's have badges," Shawna said.

Uh oh, Joey was home. He banged on my door. I'd latched it, just in case.

"No, you can't come in," I said. Then I thought of his shoe box full of badges, he collected them. He had Batman, Ghost-Buster, I-Love-Gifford, smile-face, frown-face badges, every kind there was. "Tell you what, Joey. Bring your badge box and I'll let you in."

He went and got it.

I asked him nicely, "Could we have some?"

"No! They're mine!" He shook his head ten times.

Julie and Cory laughed. They thought he was so cute.

"Are you a club?" he asked. "Can I be in it?"

My turn to shake my head.

"Come on, let him. He could be our mascot," Cory said. She didn't know what a pest he could be.

I said, "No. Joey, would you sell us some badges?"

"Okay, for a million dollars. No, a trillion. No, I know, I'll give them to you for almost free." He laughed like a gap-toothed demon. "If you'll give me your jacks ball."

"No!"

"No ball, no badges." He put the lid on the box.

"You can have mine," Cory said. "Catch!" Hers was clear plastic with an orange butterfly inside. She threw it to him.

Joey studied it, tested it for bounciness. "Oh, all right." And he let us pick four badges.

"Thanks. Now leave us alone, okay?"

We painted over the badges with thick yellow poster paint. When the yellow was dry, we painted on "NOBS!" in bright red.

79

While that was drying, we discussed who we'd have. Whoever wanted to join. As long as they were in fifth grade, and as long as we all liked them.

Then we had elections. We elected Julie Secretary because she had the best handwriting, and Shawna, Treasurer, because she was good in math.

Then I started to nominate Cory for President for thinking up our name. But she beat me to it. She nominated me, because the whole thing was my idea.

So she got to be Vice President, and I, President of Nobs!

"Thanks, you g-g-guys." I felt great, terrific. The only bad thing was how I was stuttering again. And I'd almost stopped doing that while it looked like Laura and I were going to be friends.

Cory stayed later than Julie and Shawna, and wanted to play jacks. We used my ball. And I noticed another bad thing, how I was playing.

"Hey, are you letting me win?" Cory asked.

"No."

"Well, it seems like you're not trying."

"I *am*." I tried harder. But it was no use. Something weird was going on. And I wondered: My ball was right there. But I'd broken my oath by telling Laura the Supes' secret club name. So did that mean that my ball, even though I held it in my hand, was "forfeit" anyway, and no good anymore? Was that why I kept on missing, like I didn't even know how to play?

•••••••••••

By next week our club had three new members: Heather Wynan, Megan McClure, and a boy, Alex Gardella. It would have been sexist not to let him join. Even though we suspected he only wanted to so he could be around Shawna. Because he had a major crush on her.

We won the windowsill race three days in a row and got down safe, before Ms. Tatum came in. We did great at recess, too, fighting for the climbing bars. We posted a sentry to warn us in case the playground-duty teacher headed over. So we didn't get caught, and beat them three out of five times, not bad!

Things were going great. And what with meetings, and club members calling me up all the time, I didn't have time to brood about the two things—my stutter and my jacks technique— that were going badly.

Then, the next week—disaster! Or nearly, anyway. It started in Language Arts. We'd just finished a poetry unit, and Ms. Tatum made us write poems of our own.

"Oh no," kids groaned, "too hard."

"Relax, you won't get graded on it. I'll make it easy for you. You can start with something familiar." She wrote these titles, "Rockabye Baby," "Higgledy Piggledy," "Three Little Kittens," "Rub-A-Dub-Dub," on the board. "Those are just examples. You can take any old nursery rhyme, song, or poem that you like, and change it around any way you want. Make it funny, sad, bad, angry—however you're feeling. Let yourselves go, don't be scared to put your feelings in. Feelings are what poetry is all about."

Hm. I chewed on my eraser, tried to get an idea.

I looked over to where Laura sat, as far away from me as she could get. I missed her and was mad at her, both.

I looked at the Supes. I thought about how much I hated them. Which the most? Beth, because she hated me the most? Liz, because she'd been the nicest to me, but didn't mean it? Or Vero, for coming along and being number three?

I thought about three—some "lucky" number! There it was, on the board: three kittens, three men in the tub . . .

Then I felt someone's eyes on me—Beth's, full of scorn, making fun. Like, so what if I was President of Nobs? To her I was still a nobody, spelled with a small *n*.

So then I got mad! I thought, Okay, Ms. Tatum, I'll let myself go. Shazam! I had my whole poem, loaded with feelings. It told another secret, too. But what the heck, why not? How many times could a thing be forfeit?

I wrote it down as fast as if my pencil had wings. There, done.

When the time was up, some kids read their poems aloud. Not me. I had other plans for mine.

At recess, I called the Nobs together and recited it to them.

They all asked, "What tree house?" That was the other secret.

"The Supes' clubhouse, it's in the woods behind Liz's house." And I made them learn my poem by heart. "Alex, you be the sentry."

The Supes were climbing up to their perch.

We Nobs went over there. I gave the signal. "Now!" And we sang, all together:

> "Rockabye Supies,
> On the tree top,
> When the wind blows,
> Your tree house will rock.
> When the bough breaks,
> Your tree house will fall,
> Down will come Supies,
> Tree house, and all!"

They were furious. They swung down. Liz grabbed me by the shoulders and shook me. "You swore not to tell!"

Beth grabbed me from the back. "You broke your oath. Now hand it over."

I laughed. "Sorry, I don't have it on me."

Liz asked, "Are you sure? Beth, and Vero, hold her arms."

"I don't want to do this," said Vero. "Catch you guys later." And walked away.

My fellow Nobs got me free and formed a circle around me. Liz and Beth broke through. They didn't believe that I didn't have the ball. They reached into my pockets.

Alex's whistle pierced the air.

"That means, teacher approaching," I said. Everybody scattered.

When the end-of-recess bell rang, Liz and Beth rushed inside ahead of everyone.

When I got to our classroom, they were ransacking my drawer. They'd pulled it way out. It clattered to the floor. All my stuff spilled out.

Ms. Tatum came in, crossed the room in one second, stood over us. "Who's responsible for this mess?"

Liz and Beth hadn't bothered to hang up their parkas in the closet, they'd just slung them over my chair—with their Tree-Top-Three badges still pinned on. Expensive badges, made to order, pink, with green triangles for treetops and big green number three's.

Ms. Tatum had a fit. "I *said,* no badges in my classroom!" She snatched them off, marched to her desk, stuck them in her drawer. "Now pick up that mess, hurry up."

We threw my stuff back in the drawer, pushed it in.

"Now, Liz, Beth, and Janet, *kindly* come to my desk."

She only said "kindly" like that when she was boiling mad.

"Now, kindly explain to me what that was all about."

Silence.

"You'd rather not? Fine. Go explain it to Mrs. Radwicki!" The principal.

"No, Ms. Tatum, *I'll* explain," Beth volunteered. "It's Janet's fault, she started it, she told something that she swore she wouldn't—"

Ms. Tatum interrupted, "About clubs?"

Beth nodded.

"In that case, stop right there. I changed my mind. I don't want to hear the explanation, I've had it with clubs!" She scribbled out passes. "Go tell it to Mrs. Radwicki, all three of you, right now."

Liz gave Beth a frantic look, like, Save me!

Beth went, "Please, Ms. Tatum, couldn't you

just make the leaders go instead of all of us?"

Liz gulped, like, Hey, what are you trying to do to me?

Ms. Tatum said, "Who *are* the leaders?"

"I am," I said.

"I am," said Liz and Beth.

"What?" said Ms. Tatum, "three leaders of two clubs?"

"No, only two." Beth stepped in front of Liz. "Liz, don't you remember? You were, but now it's me."

Liz said, "Oh, right, I forgot."

"Fine," said Ms. Tatum. "You two leaders, go."

When kids got sent to Mrs. Radwicki, the first thing she did was call up at their houses. I pictured her calling up at ours. This was the one time in my mom's whole day that she had to herself and could do her composing uninterrupted. I could just see the look on her face when the phone rang, and it was the principal, to complain about me . . .

Beth gave me a push, "Go on."

We were almost out the door.

"Come back," called Ms. Tatum.

Ms. Tatum believed in people changing their minds. "They should, as often as changing their underwear, because opinions can get just as stale," she liked to say.

Well, she'd changed her mind again, we didn't have to go.

"I thought of a better solution." She smiled, all pleased with herself. "You two leaders hold a summit. Talk about your clubs. List ways they're different from each other. And," like this was the clever part, "ways they're alike."

Beth and I both went, "But Ms. Tatum—"

"I know, you're not alike, you have nothing in common. Is that what you think?"

We said "Yes."

"You see? There you are! You just agreed about something! Try to be open minded. Take notes. I want a written report. By Friday. Can you do that? Because if not,"—she glanced at the door.

So we both said, "Yes."

•••••••••••

The next day was Thursday. Thursdays my parents were both not home and Joey had play group. So we had the "summit" at Beth's.

I went on the Supes' bus. Beth must have figured, bad enough that she had to have me over, she wasn't going to sit with me, too. She sat with Liz. I sat with Vero.

Vero was like in a world of her own. She had this calendar page in her notebook, with spaces for days left in March. The page next to it had

"April 1st!!!" in giant red letters, and an airplane, cut out from an airlines ad, winging down toward the shape of Florida. She counted off how many more days, wrote in "19." Then she noticed me looking.

I said, "Sorry, I wasn't trying to be nosy."

"That's okay, I don't mind. See that plane? I'll be on it. I just know it." She sounded like she was telling it to herself more than to me.

Behind us Liz was saying to Beth, "Hey, that was neat how you elected yourself leader."

"Just think if I hadn't!"

"Yeah, you're right. Remember third grade?"

"Yeah," said Beth. "I wouldn't want to go through that again."

"So thanks for doing what you did," said Liz. "I mean it."

Vero shut her notebook. Her stop was coming up.

Then it was Beth's stop.

Liz stayed on.

As soon as we were off the bus, Beth lost all her zip. Like, life was a drag when she couldn't be with Liz.

Her house was big and fancy. The first thing you saw coming into the entrance hall was a giant photo of her parents, Ted and Kay, on top of an elephant, from when they had jetted to India. And there were lots of other souvenirs, rugs, pottery, animal masks, from their travels all over the place.

We went in the kitchen. The housekeeper, Charlayne, was there. She fixed us hot chocolate and served it to us in beautiful mugs. She offered us three kinds of cookies. But she didn't say hello or anything because she was talking on the phone the whole time.

We went upstairs to Beth's room. She had her own fireplace. And a canopy bed, like in decorating magazines, and a stereo, TV, VCR, three framed autographed posters of Cameron Fairfax, and her own computer.

She moved an extra chair to her computer table for me. She said, "We might asj well start," and turned the computer on.

She typed DIFFERENCES onto the monitor. She made two columns, headed "T.T.3," and "Nobs."

Differences were easy. We thought of lots:

T.T.3 was first.

Nobs was bigger.

T.T.3 was "more selective" (Beth's wording).

Nobs met at different members' houses.

T.T.3 had a club house. "As everybody now knows, thanks to your poem," said Beth.

"Yeah, well, let's go on."

T.T.3's all lived in Hyacinth Hills.

Nobs lived in different neighborhoods.

And so on.

"Now the hard part." Beth started a new page, typed THINGS IN COMMON. "I still can't think of any. You?"

"No. Can I ask you a question?"

She sighed. "If you must."

"What happened in third grade? Did Liz get sent to Radwicki?"

"Mm hm, and she got grounded, for two whole weeks. Her parents are super-strict. They want her to be perfect, get into Harvard and Yale, be a ballet dancer and a doctor or a lawyer on the side. If she gets sent to Radwicki again, they'll make her go to boarding school. Then I'd never see her."

"What about your parents? How would they've taken it?"

"If I'd gotten sent to Radwicki? They wouldn't have known. They're in Acapulco, Mexico."

"When will they be home?"

"In a week or so." She sounded used to it.

Not like me. The one time my parents went on a trip without us, I was six, we stayed at my grandparents'. My grandma was still alive then. And I was so miserable the whole time; I couldn't wait for them to get back.

Beth snapped her fingers in my face. "Hey, think of something we can put for In Common."

So I asked her, "What's your club for?"

"How do you mean?"

"Well, like, our club is for fun and friendship."

"Oh. Well, ours is too, naturally. All clubs are. So that wouldn't count. Rats, my printer's out of paper. I'll go get some from my dad's den. I'll be right back."

I asked, "Can I look at those photos on your mantelpiece?"

She said, "Go ahead."

She had a whole row of them in leather and silver frames. Most were of Ted and Kay, on ships, in jungles, on beaches. There was one of Kay with Beth as a baby on her lap. Kay had a gorgeous lacy dress on, and a fake little smile, like she was wishing the photographer'd hurry up and finish before Baby Beth spat up or something.

There was also a photo of Beth and Liz as little kids, four or five years old, in Liz's garden. They had their arms around each other, and Beth was laughing, looking really happy. Like, already back then, the thing that made life fun and okay for her was being with Liz.

When she came back in with the computer paper, I said, "Listen, I've been thinking, fun *does* count. So does friendship, very much."

She looked suspicious, like, what's the zinger?

"Like the way you're friends with Liz. We're friends in our club, too. Me and Cory, for in-   **91** stance. But I don't know if I'd volunteer to go to Mrs. Radwicki in Cory's place. So you guys are even better friends."

Beth's mouth was a little bit open, like from surprise that I didn't have something mean up my sleeve. "So, you think we should put those down?"

I nodded.

She typed, "Both our clubs are for fun and friendship." Then she went "Phew," like exhausted from all this work. "Two things in common, that ought to get Ms. Tatum off our backs." She fed the paper into the printer, hit the print command key, and the printer started to hum.

When Mom came to pick me up, she had Joey in the car. "Hey, Janet, want to see the hugest bubble?" And he exploded a mess of purple bubblegum all over his face. Even so, I was glad to see him. Glad I had a brother.

Grandpa came over for dinner that night. We had manicotti with tomato-mushroom sauce, salad, and tortoni for dessert. He'd brought a bunch of pink and red carnations. They looked pretty on the table.

After we ate he asked me to play something for him, and I played "Santa Lucia," because he was born in Naples, Italy, and that was a song from there and he loved it. He clapped really **92** loud and said, "Brava!"

The reason I'm telling all this is, it felt really good. Like how families were supposed to be, not having microwaved Kid Cuisine like I bet Beth was having, by herself, while Charlayne talked on the phone.

Later, when I was in the middle of brushing my teeth, Beth called me up. We'd known each other since kindergarten and never talked on the phone before. So this was a big first.

She said, "I thought of something else for under Things in Common."

"What?"

"Well, don't laugh, but if Liz, or me, or Vero wanted to join Nobs, could we? Be honest."

"Okay. No."

"I thought not. So, that makes one more thing."

I said, "You mean, keeping kids out?"

"Right. Should I put that down?"

And I said, "Yes."

Vero Jencks-Norris

"April, telephone!" Mom still never called me Vero, she just wouldn't.

It was Jencks. "Vero, hon?" He liked calling me that. "Well, it looks as though your old man's found himself a place to settle down, a cute little house near the beach in Fort Pierce. Know where that is? A couple of miles down from *your* place, Vero Beach. So you should feel right at home. I hope to be all settled in by—let's see—"

By my birthday, somehow I just knew it. Right. He said, "April first."

And the day before was the start of spring vacation!

"See ya," we always said that before we hung up. This time he said it differently. "See you soon, Vero, honey." Like, more seriously, accent on the "soon."

When I came out of the kitchen—I'd taken the call on the phone in there—Mom and Norri looked the way they always did after I talked to Jencks. Like, fine, but just don't tell them about it. So I didn't.

I started counting the days. I was going down there. I knew it, I felt it in my bones.

I had to hand it to Mom and Norri that they'd

worked it out with Jencks. That must have been hard for them to do. Not that they ever criticized him to me, but I knew how they felt about him.

As the time got closer, any fool could see that they were making all kinds of preparations for my trip, like sneaking packages into the house, hiding them in their closets. What did they think, that I'd need a whole new wardrobe for down there?

They talked on the phone a lot more, too, and hung up, fast, if I walked in, or they'd change the subject. One time I heard Norri talking airplane schedules.

So I asked, "Where are we going?"

And he said, smooth as anything, "To Sacramento," like I didn't know that was the last place Mom would want to go. I said, "No kidding." I looked him smack straight in the eyes and I laughed. When I did that to Jencks it always cracked him up.

Norri kept a poker face. "Why should I kid you?"

"Is *that* my birthday surprise?"

That did it, cracked him up, and he said, "No."

Hurray. So then, finally, I could just look forward to seeing Jencks again, after missing him so much.

It had been so bad at first, I'd thought I'd die. I'd missed every little thing about him. The way **95** he squinted at the sky and took a whiff of the breeze to guess what the weather'd do. How, on sunny days, the color of his eyes matched the ocean, exactly. How he'd joke around, start everybody laughing. The noise and fun when he had company. One time I threw a bunch of empty cans around in Mom's and Norri's kitchen, just to remind me of the beer cans clanking when Jencks and his friends tossed them in the trash. Bull's-eye!

September had been the worst. I didn't hear from him that whole month. I even called up Greyhound-Trailways and asked how much a bus ticket to Florida would cost. But then I didn't know where in Florida. So when they asked me that, I just hung up.

October, he'd called me up from St. Thomas in the Virgin Islands. I said, "Jencks, how come it's okay with you that Norri's adopting me?"

He said, "Hon, you're a growing girl, you need a stable home, and, well, you know me, I'm not the steadiest kind of a guy."

"Jencks, I don't care! You're my real father!"

"You bet. And I always will be." Then there was this funny sound. It could have been the connection. Or else he was crying, which I'd never heard him do. It didn't change things any. Except, it proved he still cared about me. So I

felt better.

By then I was starting to like it up here, a little, anyway. I was glad I'd joined the club. Not because I was crazy about putting up those posters or writing fan letters. Those things were Liz and Beth's department. I didn't want to bother. I'd found out that most celebrities just hired people to answer their mail and never even looked at it themselves. The other stuff, acting clubby in school, kicking the windowsill wall, etc., I thought was kind of "goopy." I even thought that word was, too, I just said it because they did. But the tree house was great. I went there every chance I got. It was even greater than when I'd first found it, because this fantastic thing was happening—fall! I'd never seen that before. I couldn't believe the colors!

Another reason I felt better was Judy G., the sweetest dog you ever saw.

Norri got her for me. Boy, was I wrong at first, thinking he was nerdy. He was okay, a cool guy, with lots more to him than just knowing lawyer stuff and where to buy suits with vests.

The only thing I'd gotten right, right away, was how nuts he was about Mom. Like, he'd go to the moon for her, bring her back a moon rock, anything she asked him for. And she felt the same way about him. Good, I was glad for them. Not that that stopped me from wishing—especially on nights I couldn't fall asleep—that she'd get back with Jencks.

In November, Norri said I'd need to know how to skate, now that I lived in Massachusetts, and took me to an indoor skating rink. He had some job on his hands. Standing on two skinny blades on the slippery ice was impossible, and moving, even more! But he said that he was naturally clumsy, and I was naturally graceful— hey, I never knew that! And he'd learned how, so I certainly could, too.

I spent almost the whole first time on my behind. The next time I only fell down about ten times. By the third time, I got the hang of it and it started being fun.

Norri knew all kinds of things. Like, he was a walking encyclopedia on the subject of dogs. He could tell you every breed, and the names and owners of champion dogs and runners-up in all the different dog shows. When he asked what breed I liked and I said, "Mutt," I thought we were just talking.

But we went straight to the pound. And we found a dog, right away. This reddish-brown, long-haired, long-tailed female with a smart, trusting, just-a-little-bit sad look in her eyes. The moment she saw me and Norri coming, that changed to a smile, or anyway, the closest thing **98** to a dog smile you ever saw. Like she already knew I'd pick her. Like she was saying, I'm the dog for you.

I wanted to name her Dorothy because that look reminded me of the girl in *The Wizard of Oz*.

"You're right about that," Norri said, and told me that when he was a kid he'd had a crush on Judy Garland, who played Dorothy in the movie.

So I said, "Let's call her Judy G.," and Norri thought that was a good idea.

When we brought her home, she shook herself all over the new beige carpet. And rolled on it, too. Mom wasn't thrilled.

She wasn't that thrilled with me, either. Just in general. It's hard to explain. It made me feel like a dud. Like, she had ideas of how I ought to be and I wasn't living up to them.

One time we were in the car, driving someplace. Sitting next to her, all I saw of her face was her profile. I kept looking and looking. I still felt the same as when I first saw her waiting outside the school in Islamorada, that I could never get my fill of looking at her. I was just thinking, "Oh Mom, you're so pretty," wishing I could tell her in some way that wouldn't sound mushy. That's when she said, "Why are you so uncommunicative?" And it stopped me dead.

She talked a lot about wanting us to get close, make up for lost time. She talked about all kinds of things—courses she was taking, things she was thinking about, plays and movies she and Norri'd seen, people they knew.

She arranged her schedule to leave time for doing things, just her and me. Like, in the garden. One course she was taking was in landscaping, and she had a knack for moving plants around, knowing what would grow well where. Or, we'd try out recipes from her other course, gourmet cooking. Her favorite thing was taking me shopping. I didn't care that much about getting new clothes all the time. But I loved watching her get happy when clothes looked good on me—like, then she was proud of me.

I wanted us to get close, too. One thing that made it hard was how Mom clammed up when anything came up about Jencks. She'd look hurt when I even just mentioned his name. Like what I was really saying was that everything she and Norri were doing for me was still not enough. This made a kind of gap between us that we couldn't get around or across. I tried to stay off the subject. But I was always scared it would sneak into the conversation somehow.

She was my flesh-and-blood parent. Even so, it was more relaxing going places just with Norri.

One time he and I went to the New England Aquarium in Boston. That was a really cool place with a lot more to see than at Ocean Adventure in Islamorada.

Norri was friends with the chief marine biologist, Dr. Anderson. He took us on a special tour that included going behind the exhibits. You could stick your hand in and touch them. I put my finger right into a sucker disc of a giant squid, those things they have all over them, like the rubber things on the backs of bath mats. I pulled it out of there, quick, when it started to close up. We stopped at the gift shop. I bought postcards to send to Jencks. And Norri bought me this great poster called "Living Treasure of the Coral Reef." It showed twelve different layers of undersea life, also the sea surface with gulls flying over it, pelicans swooping down, and a dolphin leaping into the air.

On the drive home Norri said, "I had lunch with Frank Faber this week." Liz's father. They did business together. "He told me you swam with dolphins down in the Keys."

I wondered what he'd think if I told him that I really hadn't, and if I could make him understand. I almost started to tell him.

But he said, "That must have been exciting."

So I just said, "Yeah."

When we got home I put up my poster. Mom looked unhappy. Like, it didn't fit in with the color scheme in my room that she'd worked out so carefully.

I didn't want to bug her, so I took it down.

I put it up in the tree house instead. Liz got sore, because I had to take down a Glenda poster to make room. I said, "Look, you have three other Glendas. Beth has a whole wall of Cameron Fairfaxes. This is the first thing of mine." And I explained about my mother not wanting it in my room.

"Oh, all right." Liz could sympathize with that. Her mom was the same way.

❧

I was glad when Laura Hoffman came into our class. I thought it was cool how she said our password and answered all those questions. I was for letting her join.

This was while Jencks was still drifting around. He hadn't found a place yet. But I was thinking that soon he would, and I'd be going to visit him. And how something could happen while I was there . . . Like, he could get sick, nothing serious. But suppose he was through with Sherry, wasn't seeing anyone new, and needed taking care of . . . I'd have to stay . . . Mom and Norri'd have to let me . . .

Oh, right, very probable. But, well, you never knew. I told Liz and Beth, "You'd need a third if I ever had to go to Florida, and I might, one of these days." Besides, I never did see what was so great about having only three kids in the club.

Liz was on the fence about Laura. Beth talked Liz out of her. Those two could really argue. They were really close, though.

One of Beth's arguments was that Laura was friends with Janet.

One argument for Laura was her living so close to the pond.

Skating was great, that day. She and I got along, I liked her. Till she brought up *Dolphin Cove.*

I'd seen that show. I loved it, I was glued to the set. But then I read in *People* magazine that the star of it, Kelsey Bethune, was squeamish in her real life and wouldn't go within ten feet of dolphins. The article told how they'd used a stand-in for her, and spliced shots together for the scenes in which the girl and the dolphins swam close. What a gyp! After that I was through with that show.

So when Laura asked if that was what swimming with dolphins was like, I got really mad.

"Let's not let her join," I said to Liz and Beth in the car going home from her house. And I was through with her.

Then, the first week of March, Mom and I took Judy G. to the vet's for a booster shot. We had to wait a long time. Finally it was her turn. We were just taking her into the treatment room, when Laura burst in, carrying her dog, Max. One of his ears and one leg were bandaged up, and blood was coming through.

"Laura! What happened to him?"

Laura was crying. Her mother said, "He chased after some dogs in our neighborhood, and they roughed him up."

So I said, "You go ahead in, Judy G. can wait."

They were in there pretty long. But he was okay, no internal injuries and nothing broken. Dr. Donovan put a better bandage on his leg. He managed to walk out on his own. Laura said, "Thanks for giving him your dog's turn."

"You're welcome. Come on, Judy G."

When we came out of there, Laura and her mother were waiting for us. And Laura invited me to her house.

Judy G. was whining from the shot. Mom offered to take her home if I wanted to go to Laura's. But Laura thought Max would like the company. So I brought her.

We had a good time. Laura put pillows on their kitchen floor for Max to lie on and rest. We hand-fed him Arfs to get his strength back. We gave Judy G. some too, and they got along fine.

Then Laura's sister Mary Lou came home. She

was really upset when she heard what happened to Max. She got down on the floor with him. "You poor guy, are you feeling better?"

Laura and I went up to Laura's room, which she shares with Mary Lou. We played records. And we talked. She told me about the place she'd lived before and her friends there. I told her about Islamorada.

She was easy to talk to. It was like we were picking up where we'd left off that day we'd skated together. I said things I'd never told to Liz or Beth. Like, that Jencks wasn't rich, and we couldn't have lived at places like Caiman's Creek if he hadn't worked there. I even told her how I felt about the tree house, that it was my favorite place of anywhere in Gifford. I was starting to feel I could tell her anything.

Then she said, "I met someone you know. Mark Parslow."

First I drew a blank, didn't remember that was his last name. Then it hit me—whammo! The waterfront counselor at Mohantic.

Great. And he'd said things. Because her face was one big question mark: How come I couldn't pass the swim test? Wouldn't you have to be a good swimmer to swim with dolphins?

My fingers went to my earrings. Dolphins, help me get out of this one!

I had to explain, somehow. But my mind was blank. And my head spun around. Or else the room was spinning.

Laura said, "Vero, you don't look so good."

"I'm feeling kind of sick."

"To your stomach? Want some water? Want to lie down?"

"No thanks. I'd just better go home." My legs wobbled when I went to use the phone to call Mom. And she came for me.

ૐ

The last week in March, Mom brought home more packages. "Saks had these beautiful swimsuits," she said, grinning.

Swimsuits this time of year? She said it was always hot in Sacramento and her parents had a pool in their backyard. Good smoke screen.

It didn't fool me!

I'd be jumping in the waves, ducking under, swimming in the shimmery, clear, blue-green ocean, my kind of water that I loved and was used to, down in Fort Pierce.

It's funny how when something's on your mind it suddenly pops up everywhere. Like, kids in school were talking about swimsuits. And not just kids who were likely to go south for spring vacation. One time I passed by the Nobs' lunch table, and Julie was offering Janet a Twinky, and

Janet said, "No, I want to fit in my swimsuit." Hm. Maybe it was because the weather'd been so unusually warm for up here, so it made people think of summer.

Another explanation was, Mom had gone to Saks with Mrs. Faber. And Mrs. Faber had bought Liz a new swimsuit, so then Beth got one, too. And they'd spread the word around.

Except, that wasn't the whole story. There were too many whispers and looks back and forth. Something was up. Some kind of excitement. Or just spring vacation in the air?

On Thursday night, Jencks called. He said it was to wish me a happy birthday in advance. "Vero, hon, I'm calling you now, because I won't be able to on the actual date. I'll be on a fishing trip." I knew it was just to put me off the scent, so I wouldn't suspect anything till the moment I got on the plane.

I said, "Yeah. Catch me a big one, will you?"

And we talked about the marine forecast and how the snappers and catfish were running. Then I did my old trick, laughed out loud, waiting for him to.

He didn't. He was being so careful!

So then I said, "I'm on to you."

And he said, with a catch in his voice, "Sure you are. You always were. Well, have yourself a good one!"

"I will! See ya, right?"

"You bet."

Friday all day I was on pins and needles. I had a hunch Mom and Norri'd pick me up from school with my suitcase, and that I was going a day early. But no.

When it was finally, finally Saturday morning, Mom came in my room early, didn't object that Judy G. was on my bed, and said, "Happy birthday, *Vero.*" First time.

"Thanks!" I was touched.

At breakfast they gave me my main present, a beautiful watch, and the giveaway was, you could keep it on underwater.

"Oh good, I can wear it in your parents' pool," I kidded, "right, Mom? So, when are we going to Sacramento?"

"Monday," they said in serious voices. "We're due someplace today," Norri added. "At noon. So be ready."

"Oh? Okay. What should I wear? Should I pack anything?"

"Wear whatever's comfortable. Don't dress up." As if I would have! "Don't pack anything."

Of course not. Mom would take care of that, or already had.

After breakfast I took Judy G. and we went in the woods. I squatted down to breathe in the garlicky smell of the skunk cabbages that were pushing up out of the ground, and I memorized the shapes of ferns uncurling, and the spring green of new little leaves on the trees. I wanted those things to be fresh in my mind when I got to Florida where everything would be lush and summery.

When we got to the tree house, Judy G. had to wait below, she wasn't allowed up there.

It may sound funny to thank a place for seeing you through rough times. But that was what I did.

When I got back down, Judy G. had been so patient, I threw her a stick, "Here you go." She never got tired of that. I threw it about a hundred times, to last her while I'd be away. I got back to the house in plenty of time, took a shower, put on a soft pair of corduroys and my shirt that's almost ocean color.

At a quarter past eleven they said to get in the car. Logan Airport wasn't too far, less than half an hour's drive. Still, if the plane was at noon, I thought that was cutting it kind of close.

We took the Mass. Pike, right, that was the way.

But after only ten minutes, we got off, took another road. And I said, "Hey, where are we going?"

Mom was driving. Norri turned around, grinned, "You'll see!"

We got off that road, onto another one for a pretty long way. Then we turned into the parking lot of a hotel-motel kind of place called the Sheraton Tower.

"How come we're stopping here?"

Both of them grinned. We got out. Norri opened the trunk, took out a small carryall.

I said, "I hope whatever we're doing here won't take long. I don't want to miss my plane."

"Plane?" said Norri.

"We told you," said Mom, "we're not leaving till Monday."

*L*aura Hoffman

Rub-a-dub-dub
Everyone's in a club,
Higgledy-dee,
Just not me.

It wasn't the greatest poem, just the truth. I'd been in Gifford a month and a half, and I was nowhere.

But then that invitation came. First I couldn't believe it. *Me,* invited to a party for Vero? After I'd goofed up things again with her, even worse, by saying I'd met Mark Parslow? I thought the invitation was a hoax. I could just picture myself showing up at that place on April first with my swimsuit and all, and getting laughed at, ha, ha.

Then Janet called me up. She'd been acting friendlier to me lately. And she said she wasn't mad at me anymore. I was really glad. We talked about other things for awhile. But the reason she was calling was the party. She was invited, too!

That evening Mrs. Norris called, said what to wear, not to bring expensive gifts, told Mom directions how to get there. So it was for real. And all the girls in our class were invited.

After that the clubs simmered down. Instead of thinking up all that war stuff, kids thought **113** about the party, what they'd bring, etc. Everyone was careful not to say anything in front of Vero. Still, I wondered if she suspected.

The night before, I tried on my suit. Mary Lou said, "You look better in it than you did last summer." And she never gave me compliments just to be nice.

Once she'd said it, the mirror said it too.

"But you're not wearing those grungy green sweats over it, are you?"

I said, "They're my only ones."

So she lent me an old set of hers, blue with white trim, that still looked almost new. They fit me great. For once she envied me for something, and said, "You're so lucky. I wish *I* was going to a swimming party."

Saturday morning I got my stuff together— bathing cap, thongs, underwear to change into, and my gift for Vero.

It *was* expensive. $9.95. I'd had to borrow three dollars from Mom. But it was so right! It was this elegant bathing cap, silver, I'd never seen one like it before. It wasn't shiny, just smooth and sleek-looking—like a dolphin's head. That's why I'd had to get it. I thought that giving it to her would be like saying, Look, I don't care what Mark Parslow said, I believe you.

I *wanted* to believe her. I loved that people could swim with dolphins. I loved the whole idea of getting together with creatures who are different, maybe nicer in some ways, than humans, and maybe they knew some things that humans didn't know. And if Vero'd done it, then not just people like undersea photographers and marine biologists, but anybody could. Even kids. Like her. Like me. *I* wanted to. I hoped I could, someday . . .

"Ready, Laura? Got everything?" Dad was driving me.

We picked up Janet on the way. We'd arranged to car pool.

She was wearing navy blue sweats that made her look thinner. Her hair was loose and fluffy around her face. She looked nice.

We got to the Sheraton Tower at twenty of twelve, just when we were supposed to. Dad let us off at the side entrance of the main building. "So long, girls, have fun."

We took the elevator up to the Rooftop Health Club. We changed in the locker room. A woman who worked there put our clothes and presents in a closet. She gave us towels and said to go on out to the pool area.

The pool was huge, Olympic size. It had a glass roof over it, so you could see the sky and clouds and birds flying past. On three sides of it were lounge chairs and palm trees and leafy plants in big pots, like in a tropical garden.

The fourth side of the pool had a big sign on the floor in giant red, blue, green, and purple letters, HAPPY __TH BIRTHDAY, VERO! With the space for the number 11 left blank.

Eight of the thirteen girls in our class were already there. No one was in the pool yet. A blond, actressy woman came over to greet us. "Hi, girls, I'm Cindy." She was the party planner.

I asked, "Can we go in the pool?"

"Not yet. Let's wait for the guest of honor."

At five of twelve everybody was there except Vero. Cindy divided us into two lines to form the number 11 and made us stand in that space in the Happy Birthday sign.

"Keep your eyes on that door, girls. Vero will come through it any second now. Get ready to sing 'Happy Birthday,' all together good and loud."

———

At twelve o'clock sharp, Vero walked in. Between her mom and step-dad. Wearing street clothes. Looking dazed.

We broke into "Happy Birthday" at the top of our lungs.

She didn't brighten up, or smile, or anything, the whole time we were singing.

116 Her mom and Mr. Norris smiled extra hard.

"Thank you, girls," said her mom, "that was great. Vero'll join you in a minute." She walked her out to get changed.

The sun blazed down through the roof. The water sparkled. Everybody hoped she'd hurry up so we could start swimming.

She came back wearing a beautiful silvery suit. I thought the bathing cap I'd gotten her would go great with it, I wanted to give it to her right then instead of having to wait till later.

We all crowded around her, saying things like, "This is the greatest place," and "Boy, were you surprised, you should have seen your face! Come on, let's go in!"

I was the first one on the diving board. I was bouncing up and down, getting ready, and I saw Cindy run to the other end of the pool. A delivery guy had come in through a door there, and he handed her something. Something big, wrapped in canvas. I didn't see what it was, and I didn't care, all I wanted was to get in the water.

Splash, I leaped in. Before I'd looked. Like people always say you shouldn't . . .

I swam almost the whole length of the pool underwater, with my eyes shut, because the chlorine was really strong. Till something touched me on the side of my neck.

I opened my eyes. Hey! My heart skipped a

beat and started beating fast as a drum. I couldn't breathe. Not from swimming. I was too *scared* to breathe. Or to move. Because this big, long, clumsy white-and-gray thing stared me in the face with little beady eyes.

A dolphin!

But not like I'd imagined. It didn't look at all pleasant, or intelligent. Just uninterested. Like the only reason it had bumped into me was, I got in its way. Like it couldn't care less about getting friendly with a creature like me.

It swam away.

Good, the farther, the better. I felt bad, though. Annoyed with myself that I'd gotten so scared. So I swam after it, underwater, and only stuck my head out when I caught up to it.

"Laura!" Cindy shouted at me just when I started to touch it. "I told you to wait! Come on out." So I did.

Everyone stood at the edge of the pool going, "Look at that! What is it? Is it real?"

Cindy smiled a stagy smile. "Shh, girls, don't scare it."

Vero stood by the steps I'd just climbed out on. She held onto the railing.

Cindy went over to her. "What do you say, birthday girl? Is that the best birthday surprise you ever saw? Go on in, have fun with it."

Vero clutched the railing like for dear life. She

looked awful—sick, or scared, or both. Suddenly she let go of it. Her body bent in a funny way, like she was going to flop into the water sideways. But then she dropped onto the floor. With this thud. And lay there, her face white as the tiles.

Everything was still. Everybody held their breath. Even the hands on the clock on the wall seemed not to be moving.

Then the Norrises were there, kneeling down next to Vero. Mr. Norris felt her pulse. Mrs. Norris put her face right near Vero's to see if she was breathing.

I don't know how long it was, probably only a second, till Vero opened her eyes.

"Thank God," said her mom and step-dad in voices I'll never forget.

She sat up. Her mom wrapped towels around her to get her warm, and sat there on the floor with her arms around her while Mr. Norris stroked her hair, saying, "You'll be okay."

Then Vero got up, and they walked her to the door.

Liz and Beth ran to her. "Are you leaving? Can we come?" Mr. and Mrs. Norris asked them to please stay.

Cindy tried to reassure us. She said in a cheery voice, "Vero's okay, it was just the excitement. She'll be fine. So let's have fun. She wants you to. Come on, everybody in the pool!"

No one wanted to, with the dolphin still in there. So she went in and hauled it out.

It was made of plastic.

She dumped it in a corner and put the canvas over it.

Then we all went in the pool. Cindy divided us into teams for water ball and relay races.

Afterwards there was a party in a private party room of the health club, with streamers, confetti, birthday cake, party games, favors, the works. It was so depressing!

"I'll go find a phone," Janet said, and called her dad to ask him to come pick us up soon.

———————————

My dad took the whole week off, and it was the greatest vacation. The next morning our family, and the Parslows, went to Cape Cod. We stayed near the tip of it in a town called Truro. The Cape is very narrow there, so it was only short walks to the ocean and to the bay.

Our two families got along really well. Mary Lou and Mark hit it off, just as I'd expected. Steve and I ignored each other in a friendly way. We did fun things; we rented bikes, we hiked, we explored the different towns.

But the greatest thing was the ocean. If you come from a place like Tuscola, Illinois, which is thousands of miles inland, you can't believe it the first time you see it. And you can't even think of any words to describe it. You just stand there and look and look.

It was a different color blue every day. Some days it had high, wild breakers thundering in. Other days, just little whitecaps.

One morning it was almost smooth, with gentle waves. Max was down at the edge, wetting his feet in the foam. The Parslows and Mary Lou were farther up the beach. Mom and I were standing watching boats on the horizon. Dad came along, put his arms around us, and said, "Moving to Massachusetts didn't turn out so bad, did it?"

Friday we went home.

I'd been thinking a lot about Vero, hoping she was okay. I called up at her house, and got the Norrises' recorded message, sorry, they were out, wait for the beep, etc.

Mom had said that when people fainted it could be a sign of something wrong. So I thought, what if she got sick and was in a hospital?

I called up Liz. I thought she'd bite my head off, say something like, since when was I such good friends with Vero that it was any of my business?

"Laura, hi!" She was, like, so glad to hear from me. Like, I'd turned into a whole other person.

She said, "Vero's away. Either in Florida, visiting her real dad, that's where she told us she was going. Or they went to California. That's where her mom told my mom they were going. So I don't know. Hey, Laura, you were great!"

"What do you mean?"

"Tell you when I see you. Can you come over?"

On Saturday I went to her house. Mom drove me.

Beth was there too.

They were impressed with me for swimming in the pool with that dolphin.

Beth said, "It looked so real! How did you feel when it bumped into you?"

"Scared."

Liz said, "You didn't show it. I'd have screamed. And Vero even fainted, and she's used to them."

They looked at each other. Beth said, "Well? Are we going to?"

"Yes, right now. Come on, Laura."

We went down the lawn behind the house and into the woods. They didn't tell me where to, but I had a feeling we were going to the tree house.

"Do you still remember the password?" Liz asked.

"Yes, 'Glenda Tyrone is terrific.'"

There it was.

We climbed up the ladder steps. We stood on the platform outside the door. They made me say the password one more time and cross my heart and say "Hope to die" if I told a soul that I was here.

Liz opened the door. "You're the guest, you go first."

That's when I saw Vero. She stood at the far wall, with her back to us.

"Vero!" We rushed up to her. "Where've you been, are you feeling okay?"

She turned around. "Vero's not my name." Her face looked different, not just pale, but like something was missing—her earrings. For the first time since I'd known her, she wasn't wearing them.

She had taken a poster down off the wall and was rolling it up. "I'm resigning from the club," she said. "Here." She handed Liz her badge.

"No, keep it, we want you in, hey, don't go!" She tried to bar the way.

But Vero pushed past her and went out the door.

I went after her. I wasn't used to those ladder steps, I couldn't go down them so fast. When I got to the bottom, she'd disappeared. I shouted, "Hey, where are you? Come back!" I didn't know what was happening with her. But something was very wrong, and I was scared for her.

I called her up when I got home. She wouldn't come to the phone.

The next day, though, she came to my house.

Janet was over. She was babysitting Joey, she'd brought him along. We were out front when the Norrises' car pulled into our driveway.

Vero didn't even want to get out of the car. She handed me back my present to her, the silver bathing cap. "Thanks. It's really nice. But I won't be needing it. I don't like swimming anymore. You're a good swimmer, you keep it."

"No. Hey, please don't leave."

She was trying to make me take the cap. But I grabbed her hand, and I held onto it. That way Mr. Norris couldn't pull out of our driveway. I said, "Come on, get out of the car, for just a minute?"

She shrugged, like, what's the difference? Like nothing made any difference. Like she felt terrible and would feel that way forever.

I had to really watch my step. I'd said the wrong thing to her twice before. So now all I said was, "Stay. Just for a little while?"

She wasn't going to. But Max galloped over, like he remembered her, and he put his paws on her shoulders and licked her face. And she said, "Okay."

Janet Di Ciocchio

• • • • • • • • • •

It's hard to feel the same about a person, after you've been to her house and all. And after that person acted unselfish, which you thought she never could. Like, Beth volunteering to go to Mrs. Radwicki so Liz wouldn't have to. So I couldn't hate Beth anymore. And of all the Supes, I'd really always hated her the most. So then I couldn't hate the other two anymore, either. And, well, I missed it. Like missing the bubbles when soda's gone flat, or the salt on salt-free pretzels.

The morning after our "summit," Ms. Tatum called Beth and me up to her desk, first thing, and said, "Let me see what you accomplished."

Beth handed her the list of Differences and Things in Common.

Ms. Tatum looked it over, nodded to herself. "Yes, good." She took a yellow marker and highlighted the last item under Things in Common, "Keeping kids out." She put an exclamation point after it, in red. "That is so true," she said. "That is the bottom line. If it weren't for that, there might not *be* any clubs. I'm certainly glad I started the peace-making process. Good work, girls." She opened her drawer, took out the **125** badges that she had confiscated. "Here's yours, Beth, and here's Liz's. Just don't wear them in school, all right? Now, can we have a ceasefire?"

There ought to be a rule against grown-ups, especially teachers, saying "we" when they mean "you." And a rule against questions that you're only meant to say yes to.

"Yes," said Beth and I.

Ms. Tatum made us shake hands on it. "There. Now, how about goodwill gestures from you both, to seal the bargain?"

"Yes."

There was a jacks game scheduled for that recess. We were sitting on the steps, flipping for turns, when the Supes approached. Liz said, "Janet, we want to talk to you. Not here, though." She motioned for me to follow them to the climbing bars.

They climbed to the top. I had to stay down on the third bar.

Liz said, "You tell her, Beth."

Beth said, "For our goodwill gesture, we've decided that you don't have to hand over your jacks ball."

"That's nice of you." I had it in my pocket. I rolled it between my fingers. "Thanks, Beth. Thanks, Liz." I didn't thank Vero because this jacks-ball thing went back to before her time.

"And the Nobs' goodwill gesture is, we won't call you 'Supes' anymore."

"Good. About time," they said.

"You're welcome." I got down, headed back to our territory.

"Remember, though," called Beth, "your ball is forfeit, all the same."

Yes, I already knew.

Cory, Julie, Heather, and Megan were waiting for me to flip. I did a one-hander, the hardest thing, and caught five jacks on the back of one hand. That's, well, unheard of. Spectacular. It didn't disprove anything, because you don't use a ball when you flip. Still, it got my hopes up.

I went first, against Heather. I didn't do great, just average. Then, in the middle of Threesies, my ball bounced clear away, down the steps, like with a will of its own. It rolled across the blacktop and ended up over the drain near the swings.

I lost my turn, having to go get it. Then I sat and watched the others play. "Forfeit, forfeit" echoed in my ears.

"Hey, look who's coming," Cory said.

It was Laura, like she didn't know if she should. "Is this a Nobs meeting?" she asked.

Well, not exactly, because two members, Shawna and Alex, were sitting over on the grass, just with each other. "N-n-," I tried to answer, stuttering very un-Presidentially, like I'd been doing ever since my fight with Laura, every time she came anywhere near.

She came up to the steps. She said, "I was wondering, do you have to be in Nobs to be in your jacks game?"

"I don't n-n-know. We don't have any rule about that."

Laura said, "I've been practicing. So, could I play?"

Cory said, "Wait a sec."

We turned around, held a mini-meeting. They all said it was up to me.

I wanted not to stutter when I gave her the verdict. So I tried all the things the speech therapist and everybody else who'd given me advice all these years had said to do: Unlock my tongue, breathe in, say the first syllable of the first word, then pause, then say the rest while breathing out, etc., etc.

I don't know if any of those things helped. I think what did it was Laura's face. She had that same look as when I first met her, So what, what's the big deal if you stutter or not?

I think that's what made me not stutter saying, "Okay, you can play."

●●●●●●●●●●●

When I got home that afternoon, I gave my ball one last chance. Under perfect conditions: on my smooth, even floor, with my door latched, so I wouldn't be interrupted.

I did lousy. Okay, that was that.

I went downstairs to Mom and Joey in the kitchen. He was showing her a yellow Play-Doh elephant he'd made in kindergarten. "Here, Joey." I threw him the ball.

He caught it. He was a good catcher for his age, and started to throw it back, thinking we were playing catch.

"No, keep the ball. I'm giving it to you."

His eyes went big. "You mean it?" He got ecstatic. "Yay, hurray, thanks a million, billion!"

"You're welcome." I went downstairs to the piano room to practice. My teacher, Mrs. Giannotti, was having a recital of all her students at her house on Sunday.

I felt nervous. Like, divided in two. One part of me believed that superstitious stuff about my jacks ball. The other part thought, Baloney, it was me, my own fingers, goofing up.

Yes, but if I couldn't trust my own fingers anymore, they could goof me up at the piano, too. I started with scales. Scales are supposed to loosen you up and get your fingers on track.

Then I went ahead with my piece for the re- **129**

cital, Beethoven's Sonatina in G, and started out okay.

The thing I liked about Mrs. Giannotti was, she was a regular piano teacher. She didn't play concerts, and she didn't compose. That worked out better for me.

When I was around five years old, I'd thought that playing the piano would be a cinch, and that anybody could do it. I kind of imagined an orchestra of tiny musicians inside the closed-up part of the piano where the strings were, and that they did all the work, and that all you had to do was touch the keys.

I said I wanted to play the piano.

My parents said, "You have to take lessons."

So I said, "Okay."

They thought I was too young. But I begged. So Mom started teaching me.

And it was hard! Wrong notes came out when I touched the keys. It didn't even sound like music!

"It's just that you're a little too young," Mom said.

So then Dad tried to teach me. Same thing.

I quit for awhile. Then when I was seven and a half, they sent me to Mrs. Giannotti.

Mrs. Giannotti taught other kids, too. They
all sounded like me, or worse. So it got okay,

and I started to like it. Especially when she let me choose my own pieces to play, like this sonatina by Beethoven. It was short, but it was a real concert piece.

My fingers behaved. I only made one mistake, the one I always make, around the middle. But instead of stopping and doing it over, I went ahead and finished, like Mrs. Giannotti had said I should.

Somebody clapped. I turned around. Mom had tiptoed in.

She said, "Janet, that was lovely." She sat down next to me on the bench. Her hair smelled of almonds from her shampoo. I loved that smell on her.

"Encore," she said, like people say at concerts, when they really want the pianist to play more.

I felt pretty honored. I didn't want to play any of my old pieces that she'd heard me play hundreds of times.

I took this music down off the top of the piano. It was by her. It was nervy of me to even try in front of her.

It's called "To My Daughter." She got the idea for it when she first knew she was pregnant. Then she had that test done that tells what sex the baby will be, so she knew I'd be a girl. She worked on the piece the whole nine months. But

131

it still wasn't finished when I was born. The whole piece only took four minutes to play, but she'd been working on it all this time, and only finished it this past September.

She'd played it after my birthday dinner, September 10th. I hadn't wanted a party because I was still too miserable after the thing with Liz and Beth choosing Vero for the club instead of me. So only Grandpa and my uncles and aunts were there.

Everyone applauded. I did too, of course. But pieces that are so new can't always reach you right away. Especially if the piece was composed for you, and you're feeling like such a nobody that you can't understand why anyone would do that.

The piece started with three soft staccato *plink* sounds. Then silence. Then more *plinks*. Like a new little heart, first starting. Then came a bunch of notes, not in any key, just new and strange. Then melodies started, all eager, excited, happy sounding. Then some serious, sad ones, too. And some that were like feelings you could never say in words, but that gave you goose bumps all over.

Mom wore glasses, same as me. She took them off when I finished playing. So then I saw that her eyes were wet. "That was beautiful," she said, and kissed me.

I said, "Thanks. It's a beautiful piece." Then I got this amazing feeling. About having a stutter, wearing glasses, losing my jacks touch, wanting to be best friends with someone who didn't care about being best friends with me, all those things, and still being a Somebody, capital S. With Mom sitting next to me, liking how I'd played, that's how I felt. But most of all I felt that way from the music.

•••••••••••

The next day, when I went to the mailbox, there was my invitation. I was thrilled.

"Guess what," I yelled to Joey riding his bike in the driveway, "I'm going to a swimming party!"

That day it was only about forty degrees out. Joey yelled, "Oh sure, and this is my mooncycle, and I'm riding around on the moon." His bike still had training wheels on it. He raised up the front like for wheelies, and went, "Vrrrm, vrrrm!"

I dashed past him inside; downstairs, I told it to Mom, even though she was in the middle of giving a lesson. When something that incredibly wonderful happens, it gets even better the more you tell it to people. Meantime I was wondering who all else was invited. Was Laura?

133

I called her up. "Hi, Laura. Um—" I lost my nerve. Because what if she wasn't invited?

"Hi, Janet." And she asked me straight out, no beating around the bush, "Are you still mad at me about the task the Supes wanted me to do?"

I said, "No."

"Good, I was hoping you weren't."

I told her we'd quit calling them Supes, as our goodwill gesture.

She asked how it was at Beth's house. I told about that. I said, "The only trouble is, now I can't hate them as much."

She asked, "So, is it less fun now? Do you think clubs need to have some kids to hate?"

"It helps. That, and keeping kids out." Then I thought I shouldn't have said that. Because our club was keeping her out. I wanted to ask her to join. But of course it wasn't just up to me, all the other Nobs had to want her to. And anyway, I knew that if she'd had her choice, she'd rather join the Tree-Top Three.

She said, "My sister thinks clubs should do things."

"Yeah. More than just play jacks and fight the S—, oops." We laughed. I'd nearly said "Supes" again.

While I was thinking how good it felt to be

talking to Laura again, she said, "Did you want to ask me something? Because I was going to call to ask you—"

Then we both asked, "Did you get invited to Vero's swimming party?"

Laura said, "Yes!"

I was using Dad's phone in his study, and I knocked his desk chair over, jumping up, "So did I!"

We said we'd car pool to it, and talked about what to get her. And I think Laura liked talking on the phone to me too. But then Laura's sister said she was hogging it and made her hang up.

I called Cory. She'd been trying to call me. She was invited, so were Heather and Megan, but not Julie or Shawna. Just all the girls in our class.

Then I was still in such a great mood, I went to Joey's room and said, "Joey, do me a favor, could I borrow my ball back just for a couple of minutes?"

"It's *my* ball now. No backs."

"Come on, just for five minutes."

"Okay, five minutes."

I'd brought my jacks with me. The floor in his room was just as good as in mine. I sat down and played right straight through Sixsies and back, like when I still had my touch. **135**

"Time's up, give it!" Joey held his hand out. I gave him back the ball.

I went to my room. I got out an old ball, a plain yellow one. And I did okay, missed on Fivesies, but when I started over, I played straight through. Hm. Well, the kind of mood you were in had to count too.

April Jencks-Norris

❧

I'd seen real dolphins up close. So I knew right away that thing in the pool was a fake.

As fake as "Vero." As fake as that I'd swum with dolphins. As fake as that I was going to see Jencks.

I wanted to die. People say that all the time. But I really wanted to. God, that scared me. It scared me so much, I passed out.

When I came to, my head hurt. Not too badly. But I wanted to leave. I needed a party with kids that I'd lied to the way a person who's drowning needed a good dunking. I said, "I want to go home."

Besides, I kept thinking, the mailman hadn't come yet that morning . . .

Mom and Norri took me home. When we got near our mailbox I jumped out of the car. "Easy," Mom called. "Take it slow," Norri called.

I went tearing up to the mailbox. I figured that since I wasn't going to see Jencks on my birthday, he'd sent me a present and it would be waiting in there.

But there were only letters, ads, and bills for Mr. and Mrs. Norris.

I asked to go in the woods. I needed to be in the tree house.

They said absolutely not, and made me rest. I slept a couple of hours.

When I woke up, Norri's cousin Buddy had driven over from Cambridge. He was a neurologist. That's a brain doctor.

He peered into my eyes with a super-bright light. He did the knee-jerk thing on me, with his little rubber hammer. Then he made me shut my eyes and touch my nose with my left-hand's pointing finger. And walk a straight line backwards and forwards, like drunks have to do on drunk tests. Then he looked at my head to see if a bump was starting. "Does it still hurt?"

"No. It's just a little sore."

"She's A-okay, from what I can see," he said and winked at Mom and Norri to leave him alone with me a second.

I was sitting on my bed. He pulled up a chair, and straddled it, like to be informal, and he asked, "Is something troubling you these days? Are you unhappy?"

Like I'd tell him. Just like that, even though I'd only met him once before, at Mom's and Norri's wedding. I said, "No."

"You had a good scare, that's all," he decided.
"They make those plastic pool animals so natur-

alistic, you can't tell 'em from the real thing, right?"

Wrong. But I let him think so.

Next morning we dropped Judy G. off at the vet's kennel. And we took a plane to Sacramento, California, to visit Mom's parents.

I had a window seat. The woman next to me was nice and offered to switch with Mom. Mom accepted, sat with me awhile.

She took a long look at me. "How come you're not wearing your dolphin earrings?"

"I just didn't want to." I tried to get across that I didn't want to talk about it.

She got the message. She started talking about Sacramento. The weather would be hot. Her parents' ranch house was pretty small. We'd all have to be considerate of one another, etc. She sounded like she was dreading it.

Then Norri sat with me. He wanted to talk about the party. He thought what happened was their goof. "Your mom and I got carried away, we were as excited as kids about the fun it was going to be. I guess we weren't thinking too straight. Sorry, Vero."

"Don't be. And you don't need to call me that anymore."

"Oh? Why not?"

"I got tired of it, that's all."

139

"You did? All right, April, then. Anyway, I *am* sorry for not realizing that when you're not expecting to meet up with a thing like that, it could scare the living daylights out of you."

"It didn't scare me."

"No? Then what did?"

"Nothing. It wasn't like that. It was just—"

"Just what? I wish you could tell me. It might make you feel better."

"I can't. I just really can't." I suddenly felt thirsty, really parched, like my insides were all dried out. I stood up. "Excuse me." I squeezed my way past Norri to get a 7-Up.

Then the movie came on. It was about gangs of drug dealers fighting each other, lots of shooting and throwing guys out windows. But it was better than having to talk.

When we got to Sacramento and I met Mom's parents, they said, "Well, it's about time!" They made it sound like it was Mom's fault they'd had to wait so long.

They wanted me to call them Grandpa and Grandma right away and "feel right at home."

Mom's father had a bristly moustache the color of sand, was thin except his belly stuck out, and wore a Fair Oaks golf cap in the house, maybe even to bed, like it was part of his head. He was the manager of the Fair Oaks Golf Pro Shop.

Mom's mother had a trim figure and a young-looking haircut. Her hair was dyed to be the same color as Mom's and mine. She taught aerobics, part time, in a senior citizen center.

Mom's father took me to the pro shop. He introduced me to about twenty golfers. One of them came back in later and kidded, "Bet you don't remember who I am." Right, I didn't.

Mom's father shook his head, like, he'd expected as much, and said, "Just like your mom when she was your age."

Mom's mother did aerobics on the front lawn every morning before breakfast. She wanted me to. So the first day I did. The next day I overslept. Mom did too. "Tsk, tsk," Mom's mom clicked her tongue, like, just what she'd expected.

After her aerobics, she did fifty laps in their pool in their backyard, twenty-five free style and twenty-five back stroke. She said I should, too. "It'll do you good."

She lent me a pair of goggles. They leaked. I swam with my eyes shut. It was like swimming blind. I didn't like it.

The last day of our stay they had a party for us with cousins and neighbors. The kids hung around the pool, jumping and diving in. I sat and watched. "Can't you swim?" a boy asked me.

"Sure I can."

So he started to shove me in.

"Don't!" I shoved him back, harder than I meant to, and almost knocked him down.

The grown-ups were on the patio. Norri'd seen, and came over. "Aren't you swimming?"

"Uh uh."

"Why not?" He put his hands on my shoulders, looked at me. "Are you scared to? You can tell me, I won't tell anyone."

"No, I'm not scared to swim. I'll show you." I stepped in the pool, swam two laps, came back out. "I lost my taste for it, that's all. It isn't fun anymore."

ی

Jencks *did* send me a birthday present. It was there when we got home. A tennis outfit. That was nice of him. Even if it was two sizes too small. He couldn't have known I'd grown that much, or that I hadn't been near a tennis court since Caiman's. The card said, "Many happy returns. Love ya, Jencks." Returns? Like, to Florida, to see him? Hey, that was funny. And "Love ya," spelled like that, looked like a joke, too. But the biggest joke was, the card had a picture of a boat that looked a lot like the *Sherry*. Jencks probably hadn't noticed, and didn't mean anything by it. But I hated it. I tore it up, threw it away.

Then I got calm and I knew what I had to do.

I went to the tree house. When I took down my "Living Treasure of the Coral Reef" poster, Liz and Beth showed up, with Laura. Like they already had my replacement. And I resigned from the club.

One more thing I had to do was give back the silver bathing cap.

Norri drove me to the Hoffmans' Sunday morning. I handed it to Laura. And we were going to leave.

But her dog, Max, came over to me, like he'd been waiting to see me. And Laura wanted me to stay. Even though she had company, Janet and her kid brother Joey. So I stayed.

They had a dock that went pretty far out into the pond. Joey was stretched across it, dipping a strainer in, trying to fish for tadpoles.

"Don't lean over too far," Janet yelled to him. "Hi, Vero. Um, sorry, I forgot, Laura said not to call you that anymore."

Laura asked, "What's wrong with 'Vero'?"

"Nothing. It's just, my real name's April. And I never swam with dolphins."

"You didn't?" It's embarrassing finding out someone's a fake. They were so embarrassed, they didn't know where to look.

"So, did that dolphin thing scare you?" asked Laura. **143**

"No. I know you won't believe me. But I can't explain it."

"You don't have to," Laura said.

"That's right, you don't have to," Janet said.

They looked down at their feet. Like, what the heck do you say to someone who just told you everything about her was a lie?

I knew I shouldn't have stayed. I was spoiling their time. I asked, "What were you guys doing before I came?"

"Janet was trying to teach me Flipsies," Laura said.

Janet looked mortified, like she thought I thought jacks were babyish.

I said, "Why don't you go on with it? I'd like to try it. Could I?" At least it was something to do.

We sat on Laura's deck and flipped. Or rather, Janet did, and Laura and I tried. It's hard.

Joey came over. His sweater sleeves had come unrolled and were sopping wet. He asked, "Can I?"

Janet said, "No. You said you wouldn't bother us."

"Aw come on, Janet, please?" He held out her ball that was clear blue with little stars in it. "I'll lend it back to you if you let me."

"No. Leave us alone. Go catch tadpoles."

144   "But I want to play jacks!"

Janet gave him some spares. "Here. Go play."

"But I want to play with you!"

"Well, you can't."

He sniffled, like he was going to cry, changed his mind, gave the ball a good bounce, and went out to the end of the dock.

Laura said, "Enough Flipsies. Let's play. Janet, you start."

Janet threw. One jack got wedged between two planks of the deck. She tried to wiggle it out, but instead it dropped down. And she'd given Joey all the spares.

She said, "I'll go get it." There was a space that you could squeeze through and crawl under the deck. Janet and Laura did. I was going to, also. But on the way I stopped, and looked out over the pond. It was a pretty day. I got into a dreamy mood, thinking of summer, warm places . . .

So at first what I saw in the pond didn't register.

Hey, but it was happening! Someone was swimming, no, more like thrashing around, pretty far from shore.

And the dock was bare except for the strainer, the tadpole jar, and two sneakers.

"Joey!" I may have screamed out loud, or I only meant to. I don't remember shucking off my loafers, or running, but I must have. I do **145** remember springing forward, taking a dive, shallow but as far out as I could, off the end of the dock. It was the coldest water I'd ever been in. My arms knifed through, my legs kicked, hard, like that was what those parts of me were for.

Joey's arms flailed. His head went under, came back up.

I reached him. "Put your arms around my neck."

He did, too tight. I loosened his grip. While I did that, I treaded water, and my feet touched bottom. I could almost stand.

"You're okay, Joey. Grab my shoulders. Hold on." I swam him back to shore.

Laura and Janet waded out to meet us. By then Joey was over his panic. His teeth were chattering, but he started to enjoy the excitement, and the piggy-back. When we got to where he could stand, he reached in his pocket and held up the ball. "Look! It fell in! It was floating away, but I got it back, see?"

"You crazy idiot!" Janet grabbed him.

"You were supposed to watch me," Joey said. "I almost drownded."

"Drowned." Janet hugged him to her, tight, right there in the water.

He broke away. He came sloshing over to me, held out his hand to shake mine. And he said, ceremoniously, like he was the blond-haired kid and I was Lassie in that old black-and-white series that's still on TV, "Thank you for saving my life."

He sounded so dramatic, we all laughed.

He said, "What's so funny? It's true."

"I know it is," said Laura, and came over and hugged me. "Thanks, April."

Later, after we got dried off, Laura said, "That was a neat dive. And if you can swim that fast with your clothes on, and with Joey hanging on to you, you must be a really strong swimmer. You might get to like it again. Why don't you keep that bathing cap?"

And I did.

Now it's the middle of August.

I'm wearing the silver cap. Laura's wearing one just like it. This water doesn't sting my eyes. I keep them open. The water is deep, clear, dark blue-green.

We're heading for Twin Mermaids. Laura and I named it that. It's a rock jutting up out of Mohantic Lake about a hundred feet from shore. Only kids in Advanced Swimmers and who've passed the distance test are allowed to go out there.

Twin Mermaids has two peaks. When you stand on them you can see really far, and you feel like you're the rulers of the lake. Between **147** the peaks is a smoothed-out hollow area, perfect for sunning. We love it here. Especially when we have it to ourselves. It's our favorite place in the whole camp.

We climb up. We take our caps off, shake out our hair, and we sunbathe. We want to get gorgeous tans, so Mark Parslow will notice us more. Oh, we know it's hopeless. He's starting college in the fall, and we're only going into sixth grade. Besides, he's dating Laura's sister, at least he was, back in spring. But anyway, we have tremendous crushes on him. That's one thing that's making this summer so exciting.

Laura and I are both in "Pines," the nearest bunk to the lake. We're really friends now. She told me she was hoping for that from day one. That's the kind of thing you can get pretty embarrassed saying out loud. But we don't get embarrassed. We can tell each other anything. And everything we do together is amazingly fun. Even icky things, like privy patrol when we have to put lime down the privies, and boring things, like kitchen duty, peeling potatoes, taking out the eyes.

"We're the kind of friends, that even our dogs are friends," I said on Visiting Day when our families brought Judy G. and Max, and they chased each other all over the place.

The night before Visiting Day, Laura'd asked me, "Do you still have those earrings? Can I see them?"

I had them in my suitcase, in the box they'd come in. I took them out.

"They're so pretty," Laura said, "You ought to wear them."

So I did. Jencks had written to me that he was planning to come. I wanted him to, of course. I wasn't holding my breath, exactly. Good thing, too. Because he didn't make it.

Anyway, we're stretched out on our stomachs in the hollow space of the rock. And Laura says, "Hey, I just got an idea for the greatest club."

"What kind of club?"

"A club about dolphins. With dolphin badges, posters, tee-shirts, all that stuff. But we'd do things, find things out. Like if they're getting treated okay in zoos and theme parks, and if the tuna-fish companies are sticking to the rules about not using the kinds of nets that catch dolphins by mistake, remember when that was on the news?"

"Yeah. Sounds more like stuff for a science report."

"No, this club would be much better. I'll tell you something, April. Only, don't get mad, okay?" She sits up, so she can watch my face. **149**

And she says, "Just because you didn't really swim with dolphins doesn't mean you never could."

I shut my eyes.

"Our club can be about that," she says. "We could work on a way we could do that. Hey, don't fall asleep!"

I'm not. I'm thinking of the dolphins, their faces when they swam up to the porthole. I'm the widest awake you can be.

Laura says, "Did I tell you, my grandparents are moving to Florida next winter. They haven't decided where yet. But I'll be going down to visit them, and maybe while I'm there I can go to that place, Grassy Key, where you can do that. Or there may be other places, too."

"Maybe I could go with you."

"You mean it?"

"Yeah." Maybe I could talk Mom and Norri into a trip like that for my next birthday . . . And as long as I'm thinking maybe's, maybe Jencks could get his act together, meet us there . . .

Meantime Laura's talking about who all should be in the club. "Janet, she'd want to. And Rusty"—her friend from Tuscola—"she could be in it long distance, what do you think?"

And we go through all the kids in our grade, including boys, discuss who'd be really interested and right for it.

"Hey," Laura jumps to her feet, climbs up to the taller of the two peaks, starts waving like mad. "Look who's waving to us!"

Mark, from shore.

I climb to the other peak and wave back too.

"Know what?" says Laura, in that certain voice we only use when we're talking about him. "He's going to major in biology, and he's interested in oceanography, he told Mary Lou—"

"So?"

"So, he'll know a lot about dolphins. Like, if they're talking or singing when they make those squeaky sounds. And, like, how they show affection—" She starts giggling like crazy. "Like, you know, do they kiss, or what?" She sings, " 'How do they fall in lo-ove?' Why don't we ask him if he'd be an honorary member, or club advisor, or something?"

I start giggling. "*You* ask him."

She blushes redder than her sunburn. "No, you. Come on. Ready?"

"Wait. I thought of a name—Dolphin X. Like it?"

"What's the X for?"

"Mystery. Doesn't it sound cool? It could be for the number of kids in the club."

"Yeah, I like it. Are you ready now?"

We put our caps on. We bounce on the balls of our feet for that extra springiness. Laura says,

"I'll race you back, and whoever loses has to ask Mark, deal?"

"Deal."

Arms out, heads down. "Get ready, on your—" We can't say "mark" without giggling. "Get set, go!"

We swoop forward, bodies arching through the air. It feels like flying. Then the water lets us in. It's beautiful. Sunlight flickers through.

F
ORG   Orgel, Doris

         Nobodies &
          somebodies

$13.95

DATE			